Student Activities in
WORLD STUDIES
for Christian Schools®

Thomas Luttmann

D1368715

Teacher's Edition

Bob Jones University Press
Greenville, SC 29614

ACKNOWLEDGMENTS

A careful effort has been made to trace the ownership of selections included in this book in order to secure permission to reprint copyrighted materials and to make full acknowledgment of their use. If any error or omission has occurred, it is purely inadvertent and will be corrected in subsequent editions, provided written notification is made to the publisher.

Permission to use "Guinea Fowl and Rabbit Get Justice" from *The Cow-Tail Switch and Other West African Stories* by Harold Courlander and George Herzog (©1947, 1974) is granted by Henry Holt and Company, LLC.

Excerpts from The Journals of Jim Elliott (©1978) are used by permission Fleming H. Revell, a division of Baker Book House Company

NOTE:

The fact that materials produced by other publishers are referred to in this volume does not constitute an endorsement by Bob Jones University Press of the content or theological position of materials produced by such publishers. The position of Bob Jones University Press, and the University itself, is well known. Any references and ancillary materials are listed as an aid to the student or the teacher and in an attempt to maintain the accepted academic standards of the publishing industry.

Student Activities in WORLD STUDIES for Christian Schools®
Teacher's Edition

Thomas Luttmann

Produced in cooperation with the Bob Jones University Department of History of the College of Arts and Science, the School of Religion, and Bob Jones Academy.

for Christian Schools is a registered
trademark of Bob Jones University Press.

© 2000 Bob Jones University Press
Greenville, South Carolina 29614

ISBN 0-57924-303-7

15 14 13 12 11 10 9 8 7 6 5 4 3 2

Contents

Act 1: Changes (1100-1650)

Act 2: Challenges (1400-1800)

Act 3: Conquests (1800-1900)

Act 4: Conflicts (1900-Present)

How to Use the Activities Manual

These activities are designed to give you maximum flexibility. We have provided a menu of activities from which you can select the ones that will help you achieve your instructional goals. Before you begin each chapter, look over the activities and decide how you want to assign them. The activity codes and skill codes at the bottom of each page will help you decide.

Activity Codes

Each chapter has four to seven activities. The activity code tells you which sections of the chapter each activity covers. The code also tells you whether the activity is good for reinforcement, enrichment, or review.

- Reinforcement activities are based solely on the information in the textbook. They help students (1) to recognize and recall major terms and concepts in the chapter and (2) to "put it all together." Some reinforcement activities cover the entire chapter. (Students can complete them as they read through the chapter or as they review for tests.) Other reinforcement activities apply to a specific section of the chapter. (Students can complete them as they read the section.)
- Enrichment activities go beyond the textbook. They help students (1) to apply information from the chapter, (2) to pursue subjects they find interesting, and (3) to develop special skills. Every student can benefit from these activities, but they are particularly useful for students who need a challenge. Most enrichment activities are related to a specific section in the chapter.
- Chapter review activities help students to prepare for the chapter test. They include crossword puzzles, games, and other interesting activities that review the chapter.

Alternative Uses of the Activities

Activities are useful for more than just homework. You can make them an integral part of your classroom discussion. Your students will especially appreciate your help in completing the more difficult activities.

- Homework—The students complete the activity at home.
- Class activity—The students complete the activity in class by themselves or in groups.
- Class discussion—You help the class complete the activity together in a classroom discussion.
- Lecture—You complete the activity on the chalkboard or overhead projector during your lecture, while the students take notes.
- Game—The students answer each question in a competition that pits team against team or "every man for himself."

Skill Codes

Every activity focuses on one of seventeen skills that World Studies students need to learn. Some activities teach specific skills such as test-taking. Others teach basic thinking skills, such as recognizing terms. *Note: Each letter in the chart below corresponds to the activity letter for that chapter.*

Chapter	1	2	3	4	5	6	7	8	9	10	11	12	13	14	15	16	17	18	19	20
1. Maps	C	C	C	C,D	C	C,D	C	C,D,E	C,D	C,E	C,D	C	C,D	C,D,E,G	C,D	C,D	C,D	C,D	C	C
2. Charts						A		A								B			D	
3. Time Line				B		A								B	B			B		
4. Graphs																				E
5. Original Sources		E		E	D	E			E			A		F						B
6. Cause and Effect																	A			
7. Using Resources		B		B	A			G	A	B	A,E		A				B			
8. Bible Study			B						A											B
9. Writing											E		A							
10. Vocabulary												D								
11. Test-taking							A		A				E							
12. Recognition				A	B	B	B,D		B	D					E	B	E	B		
13. Comprehension	B	D						B,F	B		B	B	B	F	A		B		A,B	
14. Application	A,D		A		E									A						D
15. Analysis												A,B						A		
16. Synthesis		A						B							A					
17. Evaluation			D								A								D	B

Alternatives to Grading and Burdensome Records

You do not need to grade all the activities. You can complete some of them in class discussions, games, and lectures, as mentioned above, or you can use some of the ideas below.

- Check marks—Give simple pluses and minuses. You can use this information to decide borderline grades or—if you use them—"effort" grades.
- Extra credit—Let students do activities for extra credit, if they wish.
- Sporadic grades—Grade every third or fourth activity, but do not let students know which activities will be graded.
- Notebook—Make students keep their activities in a notebook. Collect the notebooks quarterly and grade them for neatness, completeness, and accuracy.

World Studies

Learning a Trade

From the journal entries given below, determine whether Peter the shoemaker is an apprentice, journeyman, or master in his trade. Write the answers in the spaces provided.

journeyman   1. "In the last year I have wandered finding work in three different towns."

apprentice   2. "Besides studying my trade, I also help to make meals and clean the home."

journeyman   3. "This is the best pair of shoes I have made. I intend to present them as my masterpiece."

master   4. "I have begun to train a young man named Malkyn in shoemaking."

master   5. "Since I have opened my shop, several people have requested pairs of shoes."

journeyman   6. "A shoemaker from town hired me to work a couple of months with him."

master   7. "As a member of the guild, I have to make sure my work is high quality."

apprentice   8. "This is my fifth year working with the shoemaker Gibbons while living at his home."

Today, people learning a trade still go through steps similar to those of the Middle Ages. Talk to a tradesperson and fill in the blanks below. If no one is available, research a particular trade in an encyclopedia or on the Internet and fill in the appropriate blanks.

Example tradespeople: Carpenter   Printer   Barber
                        Plumber   Bricklayer   Chef
                        Electrician Jeweler   Welder
                        Mechanic   Goldsmith   Carpetlayer

Name: _____   Profession: _____

Years in profession: _____   Place of training: _____

Steps in learning trade: _____

_____

_____

_____

_____

_____

_____

_____

_____

World Studies

Chapter 1   **Activity B**

Medieval Life

Englishman Geoffrey Chaucer described life during the Middle Ages in his writings. Put the answers to the following clues in the blanks below. The circled word will reveal the name of Chaucer's book.

1. What did banks issue so that merchants did not have to carry large sums of money?

2. What did new towns often grow up around?

3. What type of window covered church walls with colored light?

4. What building was the symbol of the town's spirit?

5. What type of economy uses goods rather than money for trading?

6. What rank of clergy lived in monasteries in the towns?

7. What word comes from an Italian word meaning "bench"?

8. What were used to support the thin walls of cathedrals?

9. What legal document listed the privileges of the townspeople?

10. What were men called who exchanged money from other towns for local coins?

11. What type of architecture had high roofs, thin walls, and big windows?

12. What type of architecture had rounded vaults, thick walls, and small windows?

13. What did merchants and craftsmen organize themselves into?

14. What epidemic swept across Europe in the mid-fourteenth century?

15. What did people use to cover the smell and taste of spoiled meat?

16. What is the name of Geoffrey Chaucer's book?   *Canterbury Tales* _____

1. L E T T E R S O F (C) R E D I T
2. F A I R S
3. S T A I N E D G L A S S
4. C A T H E D R A L
5. B A R T E R
6. F R I A R S
7. B A N K
8. F L Y I N G B U T T R E S S E S
9. T O W N C H A R T E R
10. M O N E Y C H A N G E R S
11. G O T H I C
12. R O M A N E S Q U E
13. G U I L D S
14. B L A C K D E A T H
15. S P I C E S

World Studies

Map Study—France

Refer to text pages 8 and 10.

1. **Label** France and use a colored pencil to **shade** it green.

2. **Label** these features of physical geography:
   Bodies of Water—Atlantic Ocean, Bay of Biscay, English Channel, Mediterranean Sea
   Mountains—Alps, Pyrenees, Mt. Blanc
   Rivers—Garonne, Loire, Rhone, Seine
   Miscellaneous—Corsica

3. **Label** the following countries: Belgium, Germany, Italy, Spain, Switzerland.

4. **Locate** and **label** the major city found on the Seine River.

5. Using the map on page 10, do the following:
   Locate and **label** these other major centers of trade in Europe: Danzig, Florence, Genoa, London, Venice.
   Draw a red line to show the path of the overland trade route from Genoa to Paris. **Draw** an orange line to show the water route from Genoa to the English Channel.

Using Additional Resources—

Use an atlas, encyclopedia, or other resources to complete the following.

6. The Gothic cathedral shown on page 18 is found in Chartres, France. **Find** the city's location; then **label** it on your map. **Place** the cathedral icon next to it.
    cathedral

7. Universities were centers of learning during the Middle Ages. Some of the earliest ones in France were at Paris, Toulouse, and Montepellier. **Find** the location of these cities; then **label** them on your map. **Place** the university icon next to them.
    university

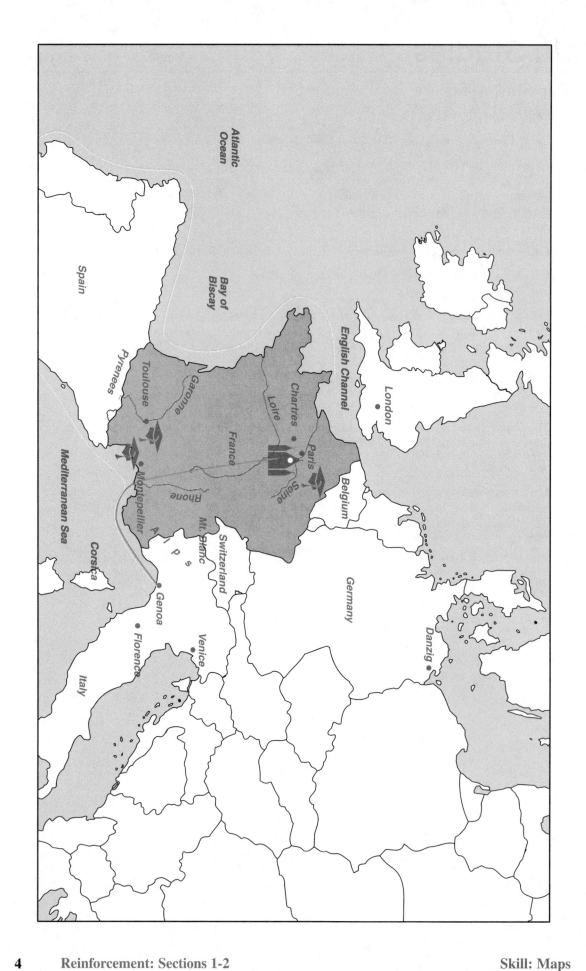

World Studies

Chapter 1 **Activity D**

Create a Town

Design a medieval town and give it characteristics that would be suited to that time. Use your text and outside resources to answer the questions.

1. Using the map above, select a site for your town. Show the town's location with an "X" on the map.

2. Why is this a good location for the town? *Possible answers: There is good transportation to and from the town because it is near a river, ocean, lake, or major road. It is protected by being on a hilltop, a closed harbor, or a cliff or by being near a fortress. It is easily accessible by being on a mountain pass or valley route. A major trade route passes through the area.*

3. Name of town: *Answers will vary.*

4. Date the town was chartered: *Answers should fall within the period of the Middle Ages (around A.D. 500 to A.D. 1500).*

5. What type of craft guilds will exist in the town? List at least three. *Examples include shoemakers,*

6. Create standards for one of these guilds.

   Guild: _Answers will vary._

   Standard of quality: _Answers will vary._

   Standard of quantity: _Answers will vary._

   Standard of price: _Answers will vary._

7. What architectural style will the cathedral be in your town? _Romanesque or Gothic_

8. What are some of the architectural characteristics of your cathedral? _A Romanesque cathedral would have rounded vaults, thick walls, small windows, candles, torches, and tapestries. A Gothic cathedral would have higher roofs, thinner walls, bigger windows, pointed arches, flying buttresses, and stained glass windows._

9. What are some of the daily dangers people might face in the town? _People might die from the Black Death. Cramped housing conditions might lead to fires and poor sanitation within the town._

10. Choose two other towns that might be trading partners with yours. _These towns could be real or ones created by other students._

World Studies

Changing Times

The Renaissance was a time of change. For each of the categories below, list the conditions during the Middle Ages, Renaissance, and today.

	Middle Ages	Renaissance	Today
Education	• few received any education • courses included Latin, speech, law, medicine, and theology	• more interest in education to make a student well-rounded • humanities are taught	Answers will vary. • education is diverse, including the humanities and technical trades
Music	• music taught by memory and used for the church and entertainment	• texts were unified and harmonies clarified • new instruments introduced	Answers will vary. • more secular music • individual composers well known
Art	• mostly relief sculptures • figures are flat and unrealistic • art mostly produced through guilds for the church	• anatomy, shading, and perspective made art lifelike • individual artists become known	Answers will vary. • nonrepresentational art has become popular
Publishing	• books copied by hand • process was slow, costly, and prone to error	• invention of the printing press • books copied easily and widely distributed	Answers will vary. • new technologies play an important role
Catholic Church	• church sent out Franciscans and Dominicans to help the sick and needy	• little help to people • lived extravagantly and supported the arts	Answers will vary. • Catholic Church has begun to support other religions
Man's View of Life	• viewed the world as a place of sadness and toil • lived for the next life rather than this one	• viewed life as offering many good and enjoyable things	Answers will vary. • modern humanism ignores God and glorifies man

World Studies

Mystery Man

On page 27 of your text, there is a copy of Raphael's *The School of Athens.* The older of the two people is supposed to be Plato, the Greek philosopher. As a model for Plato, Raphael used another famous Renaissance artist. Read the fictional autobiography about this artist's life. Using outside sources, answer the questions and find out who he was.

I was born in 1452 outside of Florence, Italy. My father was a legal specialist. Around the age of 15, I began to study under the artist Andrea del Verrocchio. This painter and sculptor taught me much. I painted an angel in one of his works called "The Baptism of Christ."

In 1482 I started working for the Duke of Milan. Besides painting and sculpting, I also worked with science and engineering. One of my greatest paintings, "The Last Supper," was completed during this time. You can still see it in Milan, although much of it has worn away.

After living in Milan for seventeen years, I had to leave. The French, under Louis XII, attacked the city. Despite my help as a military engineer, the city fell. The French soldiers destroyed one of my greatest projects—a huge statue of a horse and rider.

King Francis I invited me to France, and I spent my final years there. I was given the title of "first painter, architect, and mechanic of the King."

Much of what I learned I wrote about in my notebooks. They include many pictures of things I learned about the world as I carefully studied it with my eyes. You can read my notes, but you may have difficulty even if you know the language.

1. What artist did he study under?   *Andrea del Verrocchio*

2. Why did the author have to leave Milan?   *The French, under Louis XII, had conquered the city.*

3. What title was he given by Francis I?   *"first painter, architect, and mechanic of the King"*

4. What does this title tell you about the author?   *Answers will vary. He had talents in many different areas.*

5. Why is it difficult to read the author's notes?   *They are in another language, and they are written backwards.*

6. Who was the artist Raphael used as a model for Plato?   *Leonardo da Vinci*

World Studies

Map Study—Italy

Refer to text pages 10 and 36.

1. **Label** Italy and use a colored pencil to **shade** it yellow.

2. **Label** these features of physical geography:
   Bodies of Water—Adriatic Sea, Ionian Sea, Mediterranean Sea, Tyrrhenian Sea
   Mountains—Alps, Apennines
   Islands—Corsica, Sardinia, Sicily

3. **Label** the following countries: Austria, France, Portugal, Spain, Switzerland

4. **Locate** and **label** the three major centers of trade in Italy.

5. **Draw** green lines to show the paths of the trade routes within the Mediterranean Sea.

6. **Locate** and **label** Rome and the city that is contained within it.

Using Additional Resources—

Use an atlas, encyclopedia, or other resources to complete the following.

7. Florence was the birthplace of Dante. To show this, **place** the writer's icon next to the city.

   ✏ writer

8. One of Leonardo da Vinci's most famous works was *The Last Supper.* **Find** out which city this work is in and **place** the painter's icon next to it on the map.

   ╱ painter

9. Using a blue colored pencil, **draw** the routes of the Po and Tiber Rivers in Italy.

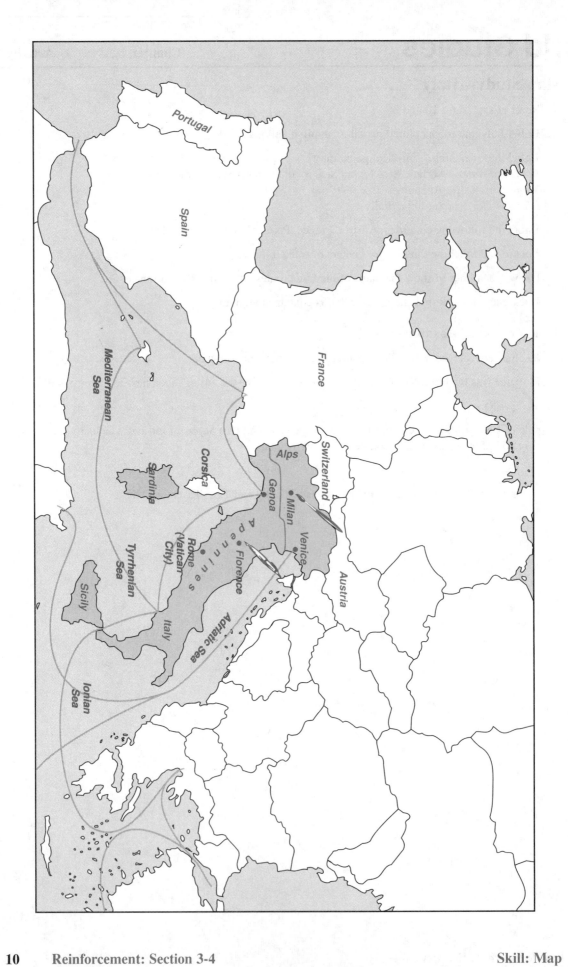

World Studies

Renaissance Art

Two important developments in Renaissance art were the use of shading and perspective. Complete the following activities and questions to see how these developments affected art.

Activity #1

1. Connect points B, C, D, and E to A using straight lines.

2. Use a ruler to find and mark the midpoint of lines BA, CA, DA, and EA.

3. Use straight lines to connect these midpoints to each other, forming a square.

4. Which of the two squares appears to be closer?   *the original square* _____

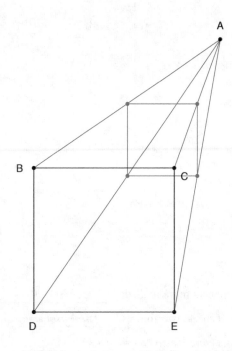

Activity #2

1. Draw a person or figure along line C. The figure should extend along the entire length of the line.

2. Draw the same figure along lines B and A.

3. Which of these figures appears farthest away? _*figure A*_____

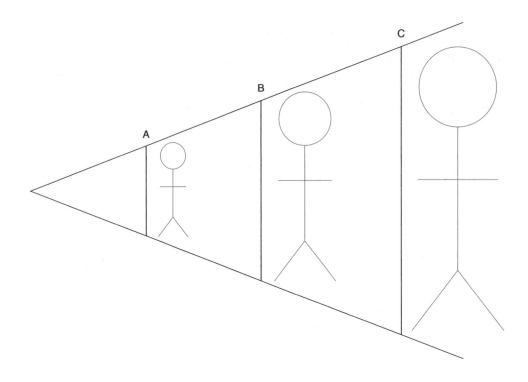

Activity #3

1. Which of these two figures appears more realistic? _*figure B*_____

2. What are the differences between the two figures? _*There is shading on figure B, giving it a*_____

*three-dimensional appearance. Figure B also has a shadow.*_____

A   B

   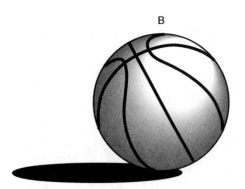

World Studies

Canterbury Tales

The following passage is a modern translation of part of the *Canterbury Tales* by Geoffrey Chaucer. The passage describes a pardoner, a person from the Roman Catholic Church who sold papers that were supposed to forgive people from their sins. Read the passage, and then in groups of three or more complete the discussion questions.

There was a PARDONER of Rouncivalle*
With him, of the blessed Mary's hospital,
But now come straight from Rome (or so said he).
Loudly he sang, "Come hither, love, to me."*
While the Summoner's counterbass trolled out profound–*
No trumpet blew with half so vast a sound.
This Pardoner had hair as yellow as wax,
But it hung as smoothly as a hank* of flax.
His locks trailed down in bunches from his head,
And he let the ends about his shoulders spread,
But in thin clusters, lying one by one.
Of hood, for rakishness,* he would have none,
For in his wallet* he kept it safely stowed.
He traveled, as he thought, in the latest mode,
Disheveled. Save for his cap, his head was bare,
And in his eyes he glittered like a hare.
A Veronica* was stitched upon his cap,
His wallet lay before him in his lap
Brimful of pardons from the very seat
In Rome. He had a voice like a goat's bleat.
He was beardless and would never have a beard.
His cheek was always smooth as if just sheared. . . .
No pardoner could beat him in the race,
For in his wallet he had a pillow case
Which he represented as Our Lady's veil;
He said he had a piece of the very sail
St. Peter, when he fished in Galilee
Before Christ caught him, used upon the sea.
He had a latten* cross embossed with stones
And in a glass he carried some pig's bones,
And with these holy relics, when he found
Some village parson grubbing his poor ground,
He would get more money in a single day
Than in two months would come the parson's way.
Thus with his flattery and his trumped-up stock*
He made dupes* of the parson and his flock.
But though his conscience was a little plastic*
He was in church a noble ecclesiastic.
Well could he read the Scripture or saint's story,
But best of all he sang the offertory,
For he understood that when this song was sung,
Then he must preach, and sharpen up his tongue
To rake in cash, as well he knew the art,
And so he sang out gaily, with full heart.

Pardoner of Rouncivalle: He was commissioned to raise money for the convent of the Blessed Mary of Rouncivalle in London.

"Come . . . me": from a popular song, perhaps a parody of Song of Solomon 4:8

the . . . profound: The Summoner sang a strong bass.

hank: bunch of strands

rakishness: stylish appearance

wallet: knapsack

A Veronica: kerchief of St. Veronica with which she wiped the face of Christ and which retained the image of His face.

latten: copper alloy (fake gold)

trumped-up stock: counterfeit wares

dupes: fools (deceived persons)

plastic: easily changed

In groups, discuss and complete the following:

1. What was the purpose for the Pardoner's visit? *to raise money for the convent of the Blessed Mary of Rouncivalle in London*

2. Give a description of what the Pardoner looks like based on what you have read about him. What does his appearance tell you about his character? *The Pardoner had locks of yellow hair that hung to his shoulders. He did not wear a hood because he thought it was not stylish. The only thing he wore on his head was a small cap which had a Veronica kerchief on it. His face was beardless and smooth, and his eyes had a glitter. Besides his wallet of pardons, he carried with him several relics. Outside appearances were very important to the Pardoner. His clean look and his relics were ways of showing the people he was supposedly fit to grant pardons from sin.*

3. How did the Pardoner make "dupes of the parson and his flock"? *The Pardoner fooled the people by flattering them. His eloquent speech and saintly appearance made the people trust him more. He also fooled them by pretending to have real relics from the Bible and from saints. The biggest way he fooled them was by convincing them they could have their sins forgiven by buying his pardons.*

4. What does it mean when it says "his conscience was a little plastic"? *If it helped him raise more money, the Pardoner might change his views on what was right and wrong.*

5. What did the Pardoner do best? Why was this important for him? *The Pardoner was best at singing the offertory. He knew this was his best opportunity to preach to the people, convincing them to buy pardons and give money to the church project.*

6. Compare the Pardoner with the description of the Roman Catholic Church during the Renaissance. *During the Renaissance the church was more interested in power and politics than in helping people. Similarly, the Pardoner's main interest was raising money, not helping people who wanted their sins forgiven. One of the main interests of the church at this time was art. Many great buildings and works of art were supported by the church. In this passage the Pardoner is trying to raise money for a building project in Rouncivalle.*

World Studies

In each numbered line, underline the word that is least related to the bold word.

1. **Martin Luther**

   Diet of Worms   <u>Anglican Church</u>   Germany   Ninety-five Theses

2. **France**

   Calvinists   St. Bartholomew's Day   Huguenots   <u>Hussites</u>

3. **Johann Sebastian Bach**

   Germany   <u>mannerism</u>   composer   Protestant Church

4. **Church of England**

   <u>Charles V</u>   Henry VIII   Elizabeth I   Edward VI

5. **pope**

   indulgences   St. Peter's Basilica   <u>Protestant</u>   excommunication

6. **John Knox**

   <u>"the Theologian"</u>   Mary, Queen of Scots   reformer   Presbyterian Church

7. **mannerism**

   contorted figures   movement   <u>warmth</u>   confined space

8. **George Frederick Handel**

   baroque   England   *Messiah*   <u>chiaroscuro</u>

9. **John Calvin**

   France   Switzerland   <u>outlaw</u>   "Reformed" Church

10. **astronomy**

    <u>William Harvey</u>   Copernicus   telescope   Galileo Galilei

World Studies

Chapter 3   Activity B

Doctrines of the Reformation

Three key Bible doctrines were taught during the Reformation: (1) *the authority of Scripture,* (2) *justification by faith,* and (3) *the priesthood of the believer.* Read each verse, decide which doctrine it refers to, and place the reference under that heading.

References:

Romans 3:28
I Thessalonians 2:13
I Peter 2:9
Isaiah 40:8
Galatians 3:24
I Timothy 2:5
Revelation 1:6
John 5:39
Romans 10:9
Titus 3:5

I Peter 2:5
Ephesians 2:8, 9
II Timothy 3:16
Revelation 5:10
John 17:17
Hebrews 4:14-16
II Peter 1:21
Romans 8:34
Galatians 1:6-8
Romans 5:1
Galatians 2:16

Authority of Scripture	Justification by Faith	Priesthood of the Believer
I Thessalonians 2:13	Romans 3:28	Hebrews 9:15
II Timothy 3:16	Galatians 3:24	Revelation 5:10
John 5:39	Galatians 2:16	I Peter 2:5
John 17:17	Romans 10:9	I Timothy 2:5
II Peter 1:21	Ephesians 2:8, 9	Revelation 1:6
Isaiah 40:8	Romans 5:1	Hebrews 4:14-16
Galatians 1:6-8	Titus 3:5	Romans 8:34

World Studies

Map Study—Germany

Refer to text pages 51 and 52.

1. **Label** Germany and use a colored pencil to **shade** it orange.

2. **Label** these features of physical geography:
   Bodies of Water—Baltic Sea, North Sea
   Rivers—Elbe, Rhine, Weser
   Miscellaneous—Bavarian Alps, Black Forest

3. **Label** the following countries: Austria, Belgium, Czech Republic, Denmark, France, Luxembourg, the Netherlands, Poland, Switzerland, the United Kingdom.

4. **Locate** and **label** the following places connected with Martin Luther:
   Wittenberg—where the Ninety-five Theses were posted
   Worms—where Luther was brought to trial
   Wartburg—where Luther began translating the Bible into German

5. **Locate** Berlin and **label** it with a star to show it is the capital of Germany.

Using Additional Resources—

Use an atlas, encyclopedia, or other resources to complete the following.

6. **Find** the city of Geneva; then **label** it on the map. What famous reformer was from here? **Place** his name and the reformer's icon by the city.

    reformer

7. **Place** the appropriate icons and the names of the following men in the countries they were from: Nicolas Copernicus, Johann Sebastian Bach, William Harvey, John Knox.

    scientist

    composer

8. **Find** the city of Trent where the church council took place. **Label** the city.

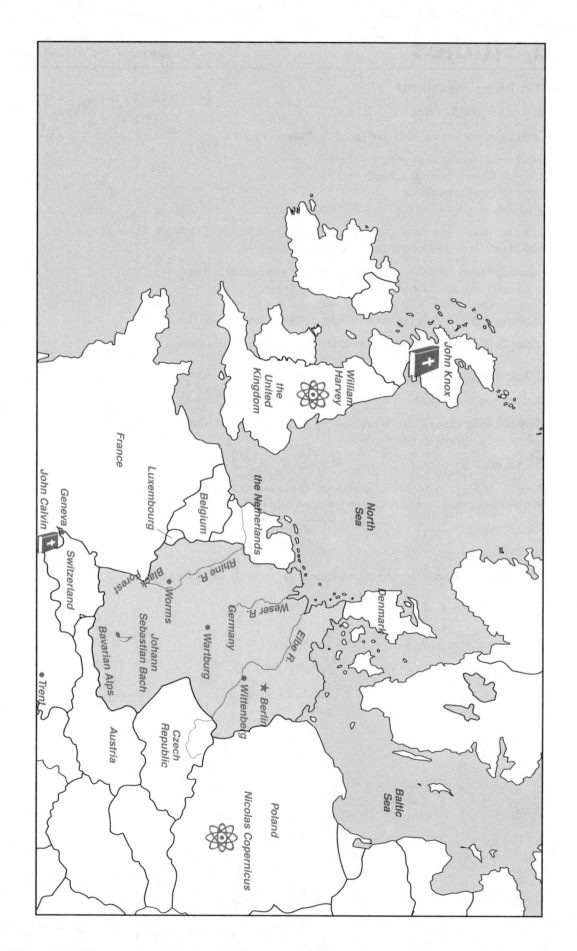

World Studies

Chapter 3　　　**Activity D**

Baroque Art

Compare and contrast paintings A and B (on the next page) by answering the following questions. Both paintings depict Michael the archangel overcoming Satan.

1. Which painting shows more movement among the figures?　*B*

2. In what ways does the artist use Michael to show movement?　*Michael's arm is outstretched, ready to strike with the sword. The folds of his cloak seem to be moving in the air and his wings are spread out.*

3. In what ways does the artist show movement through Satan?　*Satan's arms are bent, and it looks like his hands are clinging to the side of a pit. The wings on his back are outstretched and his head is turned.*

4. Describe the background elements in both pictures.　*Painting A's background is nondescript except for a circle-tiled floor. Painting B's background shows clouds, rocks, and fire.*

5. Compare the eyes of Michael in paintings A and B. Where is he looking in each painting?　*In painting A, Michael looks out toward the viewer. He doesn't seem to notice Satan under his foot. In painting B, Michael is looking down toward Satan. There is a connection between the two figures through his focus.*

6. Page 68 of your text mentions a technique called chiaroscuro. Which painting demonstrates this technique?　*B*

7. Which of the two paintings was done in the baroque style?　*B*

A

Master of Benabbio. Detail from *Madonna and Child with Michael the Archangel, St. John the Evangelist, St. Blaise and St. Peter.* (The Bob Jones University Collection)

B

Giovanni Andrea Sirani. *Michael Overcoming Satan* (The Bob Jones University Collection)

World Studies

Chapter 4   **Activity A**

Mongol Trivia

Play this trivia game with a friend to review the chapter material. Answers may be found on the text-book pages listed. Keep track of the question point values and place the totals in the boxes below.

Point Values	Genghis Khan	Mongol Culture	Empire after Genghis	Outsiders
100	What does his title mean? (p. 82) *"Universal Ruler"*	What was used to cover tent frames? (p. 88) *felt*	Which Mongol ruler defeated the Chinese? (p. 97) *Kublai Khan*	What important Christian group was in the Mongol Empire? (p. 95) *the Nestorians*
200	What were his postmen called? (p. 85) *arrow riders*	Who was the supreme god of the Mongols? (p. 95) *Tengri*	Which ruler was named for his disability? (p. 100) *Tamerlane*	What island group did Kublai fail to conquer? (p. 98) *Japan*
300	What tricky warfare tactic did he use? (p. 85) *pretend retreat*	What is the name for round Mongol tents? (p. 88) *yurts*	What was Akbar's famous building? (p. 100) *the Taj Mahal*	Who wrote the poem *Kublai Khan*? (p. 97) *Samuel Coleridge*
400	What was his law code called? (p. 82) *the Great Yasa*	What was the camp of a general called? (p. 88) *an ordu*	What were the Mongols in Russia called? (p. 99) *the Golden Horde*	What was the European name for a Mongol? (p. 99) *Tartar*
500	What material was used in his soldiers' shirts? (p. 83) *raw silk*	What is the name for a Mongol priest? (p. 95) *a shaman*	What Mongol dynasty was in India? (p. 100) *the Mughul dynasty*	What area did Batu conquer much of? (p. 99) *Russia*
600	What year was he born? (p. 82) *1162*	What Mongol drink is made of mare's milk? (p. 90) *kumiss*	What Mongol dynasty was in China? (p. 97) *the Yuan dynasty*	What famous Italian was in China in the 1300s? (p. 96) *Marco Polo*

Names	Scores

World Studies

East Meets West Time Line

Use your book, an encyclopedia, or a dictionary to find the dates of the following events. Then correctly place the event on the timeline. Use a red pen or pencil to show dates from the East and a blue pen or pencil to show dates from the West.

EAST

1279	Kublai Khan establishes the Yuan dynasty
1162	Genghis Khan born
1206	Genghis Khan unites Mongols
1243	Batu Khan rules in Moscow
1556	Akbar begins his rule in India
1398	Tamerlane invades India

WEST

1095	Beginning revival of towns; Crusades began
1215	Magna Carta signed by King John of England
1517	Luther's Ninety-five Theses posted
1275	Marco Polo in service to Kublai Khan
1456	Gutenberg's first Bible printed
1564	Shakespeare born
1350	Renaissance begins

EAST	MEETS	WEST
	1000s	1095—Beginning revival of towns; Crusades begin
1162—Genghis Khan born	1100s	
1206—Genghis Khan unites Mongols 1243—Batu Khan rules in Moscow 1279—Kublai Khan establishes the Yuan dynasty	1200s	1215—Magna Carta signed by King John of England 1275—Marco Polo in service to Kublai Khan
1398—Tamerlane invades India	1300s	
	1400s	1456—Gutenberg's first Bible printed
1556—Akbar begins his rule in India	1500s	1517—Luther's Ninety-five Theses posted 1564—Shakespeare born

World Studies

Map Study—Central Asia

Refer to text pages 86-87.

1. **Label** these features of physical geography:
   Bodies of Water—Aral Sea, Caspian Sea
   Mountains—Altai, Himalayas, Kunlun Shan, Tien Shan
   Deserts—Gobi, Taklimakan

2. **Label** the following countries: Kazakhstan, Kyrgyzstan, Mongolia, Tajikistan, Turkmenistan, Uzbekistan.

3. **Label** the three regions of China included in Central Asia.

4. **Place** the Lamaism icon in the three areas on the map where the religion is followed.

   𝓛 Lamaism

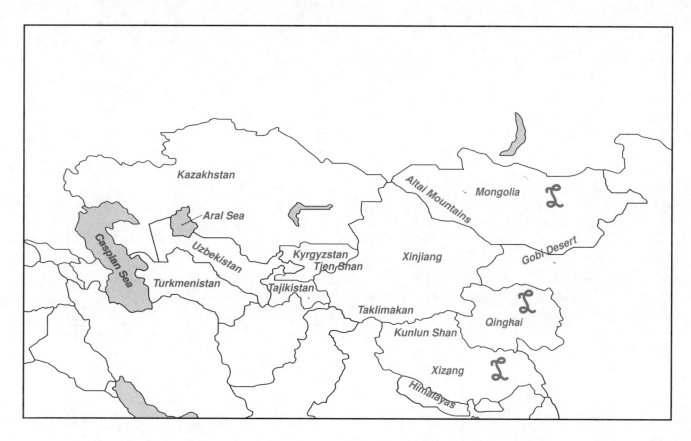

World Studies

Mongol Empire

Refer to text pages 97 and 100.

1. Use a green colored pencil to **trace** the borders of the Mongol Empire and to **shade** it.

2. **Label** these features on the map:
   Continents—Africa, Asia, Europe
   Cities—Baghdad, Constantinople, Kiev, Moscow, Novgorod

3. Use a red colored pencil to **trace** the borders of Tamerlane's Empire and to **draw** vertical lines there.

4. Use a yellow colored pencil to **trace** the borders of the Mughul Empire and to **shade** it.

5. **Label** these features on the map:
   Bodies of Water—Arabian Sea, Bay of Bengal, Indian Ocean, Mediterranean Sea, Persian Gulf
   Regions—Arabia, Cathay, India, Mongolia, Russia

Using Additional Resources—

Use an atlas, encyclopedia, or other resources to complete the following.

6. Use a blue colored pencil to **trace** or **draw** the routes of the various rivers shown on pages 97 and 100. **Find** the names of the rivers and **label** them.

7. The Taj Mahal, shown on page 101, is located in Agra, India. **Find** this city and then **label** it on your map.

8. Tamerlane's capital was located in modern-day Uzbekistan in the city of Samarkand. **Find** this city and then **label** it on your map.

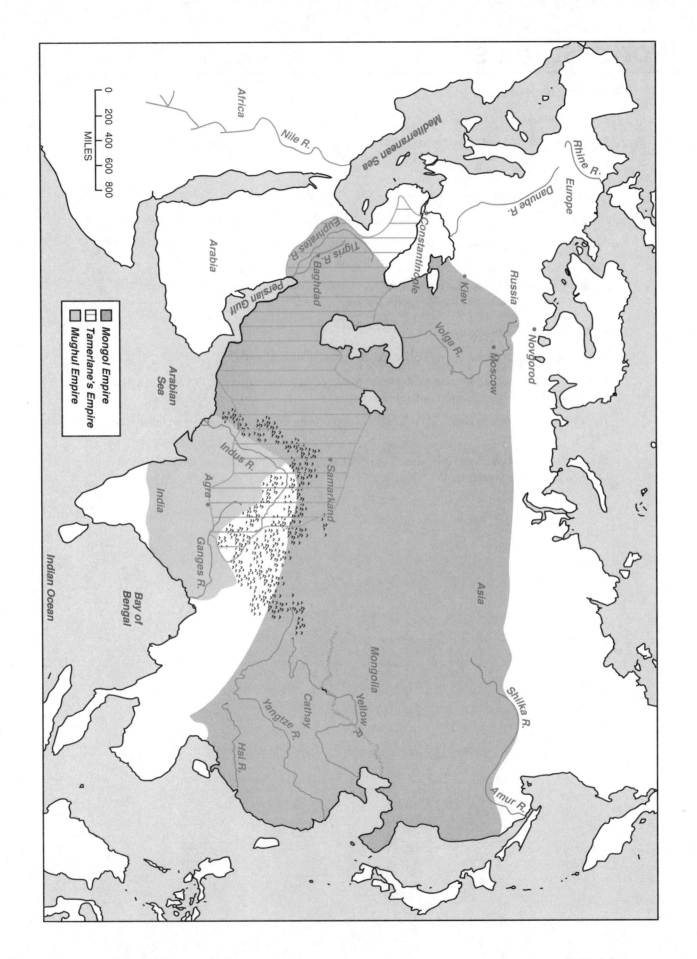

Legend:
- Mongol Empire
- Tamerlane's Empire
- Mughul Empire

Map labels: Africa, Nile R., Mediterranean Sea, Rhine R., Europe, Danube R., Russia, Constantinople, Kiev, Volga R., Novgorod, Moscow, Arabia, Euphrates R., Tigris R., Baghdad, Persian Gulf, Arabian Sea, Indus R., Agra, India, Ganges R., Samarkand, Asia, Indian Ocean, Bay of Bengal, Shilka R., Mongolia, Yellow R., Cathay, Yangtze R., Hsi R., Amur R.

MILES
0 200 400 600 800

World Studies

Mongol Invasion

During Marco Polo's time, Japan was known as Zipangu. In groups, read his account of Kublai Khan's attempt to conquer Japan, and answer the questions at the end. Remember the other name for Mongols.

Zipangu is an island in the eastern ocean, situated at the distance of about fifteen hundred miles from the mainland, or coast of Manji. It is of considerable size; its inhabitants have fair complexions, are well made, and are civilized in their manners. Their religion is the worship of idols. They are independent of every foreign power, and governed only by their own kings. They have gold in the greatest abundance, its sources being inexhaustible, but as the king does not allow of its being exported, few merchants visit the country, nor is it frequented by much shipping from other parts. To this circumstance we are to attribute the extraordinary richness of the sovereign's palace, according to what we are told by those who have access to the place. The entire roof is covered with a plating of gold, in the same manner as we cover houses, or more properly churches, with lead. The ceilings of the halls are of the same precious metal; many of the apartments have small tables of pure gold, of considerable thickness; and the windows also have golden ornaments. So vast, indeed are the riches of the palace, that it is impossible to convey an idea of them. In this island there are pearls also in large quantities, of red (pink) colour, round in shape, and of great size, equal in value to, or even exceeding that of white pearls. . . . There are also found there a number of precious stones.

True or False

False   1. Japan was ruled by the kings of Manji.

False   2. Japan was a major center of trade in the East.

True   3. The people of Japan were civilized.

4. Do you think all of Marco Polo's information is accurate? Why or why not?   _No; he exaggerates the riches of Japan by saying the gold sources are inexhaustible. His description of the palace is based on what he has heard, not what he has seen._

5. How do you think a European in the Middle Ages would react after reading about Japan?   _Answers will vary. Europeans may have become excited at the thought of the riches of the East._

Of so great celebrity was the wealth of this island, that a desire was excited in the breast of the grand khan Kublai, now reigning, to make a conquest of it, and to annex it to his dominions. In order to effect this, he fitted out a numerous fleet, and embarked a large body of troops, under the command of two principal officers, one of whom was named Abbacatan, and the other Vonsancin. The expedition sailed from the ports of Zai-tun and Kinsai, and, crossing the intermediate sea, reached the island in safety; but in consequence of a jealousy that arose between the two commanders, one of whom treated the plans of the other with contempt and resisted the execution of his orders, they were unable to gain possession of any city or fortified place, with the exception of one only, which was carried by assault, the garrison having refused to surrender. . . . It happened, after some time, that a north wind began to blow with great force, and the ships of the Tartars, which lay near the shore of the island, were driven foul of each other. It was determined thereupon, in a council of the officers on board, that they ought to disengage themselves from the land; and accordingly, as soon as the troops were re-embarked, they stood out to sea. The gale, however, increased to so violent a degree that a number of the vessels foundered. The people belonging to them, by floating upon pieces of the wreck, saved themselves upon an island lying about four miles from the coast of Zipangu.

The other ships . . . directed their course homewards, and returned to the grand khan. Those Tartars who remained upon the island where they were wrecked, and who amounted to about thirty thousand men, finding themselves left without shipping, abandoned by their leaders, and having neither arms nor provisions, expected nothing less than to become captives or to perish; especially as the island afforded no habitations where they could take shelter and refresh themselves.

True or False

True   6. Kublai Khan wanted to conquer Japan because of its riches.

False   7. The Mongols lack of supplies prevented them from capturing the Japanese cities and forts.

False   8. The Mongol forces left Japan because an astrologer predicted their defeat.

9. How do you think the Japanese might have explained the Mongol defeat?   *Answers will vary. The*
   Japanese did credit the defeat to divine intervention.

10. Look up the word *kamikaze* in a dictionary. Write down any information you can find about what the
    word means and where it comes from. Kamikaze: *a Japanese pilot in World War II trained to make a*
    suicidal crash attack, especially upon a ship; kami, divine + kaze, wind (the legendary name of a typhoon
    that in 1281 destroyed the Mongol navy)

As soon as the gale ceased and the sea became calm, the people from the main island of Zipangu came over with a large force, in numerous boats, in order to make prisoners of these shipwrecked Tartars, and having landed, proceeded in search of them, but in a straggling, disorderly manner. The Tartars on their part, acted with prudent circumspection, and, being concealed from view by some high land in the center of the island, whilst the enemy were hurrying in pursuit of them by one road, made a circuit of the coast by another, which brought them to the place where the fleet of boats was at anchor. Finding these all abandoned, but with their colours flying, they instantly seized them, and pushing off from the island, stood for the principal city of Zipangu, into which, from the appearance of the colours, they were suffered to enter unmolested. Here they found few of the inhabitants besides women, whom they retained for their own use, and drove out all others. When the king was apprised of what had taken place, he was much afflicted, and immediately gave directions for a strict blockade of the city, which was so effectual that not any person was suffered to enter or to escape from it, during six months that the siege continued. At the expiration of this time, the Tartars, despairing of succour, surrendered upon the condition of their lives being spared. These events took place in the course of the year 1281.

True or False

True   11. The Mongols were forced to surrender because of a blockade on the city.

False   12. All of the captured Mongols were executed.

False   13. The Japanese siege on the city that the Mongols had taken over lasted one year.

14. How did the Mongols escape from the island?   *While the Japanese were pursuing them, the Mongols*
    circled the island and stole the Japanese ships.

15. Why where the Mongols able to capture the main city of Japan?   *Most of the inhabitants were gone*
    from the city. The Mongols tricked the Japanese by sailing in ships flying the colors of Japan.

World Studies

Oral History

Oral history is important to many other cultures besides African. Find out if oral history has been handed down in your family. Talk to family members and try to fill in the blanks below. *You could expand this assignment to include more interviews and perhaps a photo album. This chapter should be covered within a few weeks of Thanksgiving, when many families gather. This will give students opportunity to interview family members.*

Mother

name: _____   birthdate: _____

childhood home: _____

brothers or sisters: _____

happiest childhood memory: _____

pets: _____

first job: _____   starting salary: _____

most famous person you've met: _____

humorous or exciting story: _____

_____

_____

Father

name: _____   birthdate: _____

childhood home: _____

brothers or sisters: _____

happiest childhood memory: _____

pets: _____

first job: _____   starting salary: _____

most famous person you've met: _____

humorous or exciting story: _____

_____

_____

Grandmother

name: _____   birthdate: _____

childhood home: _____

brothers or sisters: _____

happiest childhood memory: _____

pets: _____

first job: _____   starting salary: _____

most famous person you've met: _____

humorous or exciting story: _____

_____

_____

Grandfather

name: _____ birthdate: _____

childhood home: _____

brothers or sisters: _____

happiest childhood memory: _____

pets: _____

first job: _____ starting salary: _____

most famous person you've met: _____

humorous or exciting story: _____

_____

_____

Other relative

name: _____ birthdate: _____

childhood home: _____

brothers or sisters: _____

happiest childhood memory: _____

pets: _____

first job: _____ starting salary: _____

most famous person you've met: _____

humorous or exciting story: _____

_____

_____

   Another way families pass on a bit of their history is through heirlooms. Heirlooms are valued possessions handed down from generation to generation. Describe below any heirlooms your family has.

furniture: _____

jewelry: _____

clothing: _____

books: _____

glassware: _____

silverware: _____

tools: _____

other: _____

1. How has oral history played a part in your family's history?   *Answers will vary.*

_____

_____

2. What would you especially want your descendants to remember about your family heritage? _____

_____

_____

World Studies

Make the Statement Correct

Underline the word or phrase that makes the statement correct.

1. A (*clan, tribe*) included everyone who could trace his ancestry to a common relative.

2. The belief that spirits live in trees, rocks, rivers, and mountains is called (*animism, demonism*).

3. An interesting fact about the (*Church of the Redeemer of the World, Church of St. George*) is that it was built inside a hill of lava rock.

4. After introducing Christianity to the king and people, (*Frumentius, Mansa Musa*) was ordained the bishop of the Ethiopian church.

5. Once a city larger than Rome, (*Lalibela, Timbuktu*) is now only a small town in the nation of Mali.

6. The Greeks gave (*Aksum, Ghana*) the name *Ethiopia,* which comes from the Greek word meaning "burnt face."

7. In Benin, (*masks, bronze plaques*) were used to commemorate the life of the people.

8. The (*storytellers, witch doctors*) were called *griots* in western Africa.

9. Many people in the East African kingdoms spoke (*Songhai, Swahili*), a mixture of Arabic, Persian, Portuguese, Indian, and Bantu.

10. At the age of initiation, children learned about their family through (*oral history, "talking drums"*).

11. The main items in the trans-Saharan trade system were gold and (*salt, diamonds*).

12. West and East Africa have (*few, many*) natural resources.

13. In traditional African religion, the people worship (*the High God, evil spirits*).

14. Land that is not used for a few years is called (*fallow, nomad*).

15. In traditional African dances, men and women dance (*together, separately*).

World Studies

Map Study—West and East Africa

Refer to text page 110.

1. Use a green colored pencil to **trace** the border of West Africa and to **shade** it.

2. Use a yellow colored pencil to **trace** the border of East Africa and to **shade** it.

3. **Label** these features of physical geography:
   Lakes—Lake Chad, Lake Nyasa, Lake Tanganyika, Lake Victoria
   Other Bodies of Water—Atlantic Ocean, Indian Ocean, Gulf of Aden, Mediterranean Sea, Red Sea
   Miscellaneous—Sahara

4. **Label** the following countries in West Africa: Benin, Burkina Faso, Côte d'Ivoire, Gambia, Ghana, Guinea, Guinea-Bissau, Liberia, Nigeria, Senegal, Sierra Leone, Togo.

5. **Label** the following countries in East Africa: Burundi, Djibouti, Eritrea, Ethiopia, Kenya, Rwanda, Somalia, Sudan, Tanzania, Uganda.

6. Use a blue colored pencil to **trace** the path of the Nile River. **Label** both branches.

7. Using the map on page 115, complete the following:
   Use a red colored pencil to **shade** the Kingdom of Kush.
   Label the Kush and Aksum kingdoms
   Locate and **label** the three important cities during this time.

Using Additional Resources—

Use an atlas, encyclopedia, or other resource to complete the following.

8. **Find** the paths of the Congo and Niger Rivers in Africa. Use a blue colored pencil to **draw** their routes.

9. **Find** the modern city of Timbuktu (Tombouctou) and then **label** it on your map.

10. **Place** the church icon inside the modern country where Lalibela was located.

     church

11. **Place** the caravan icon in the modern country where Taghaza was located.

     caravan

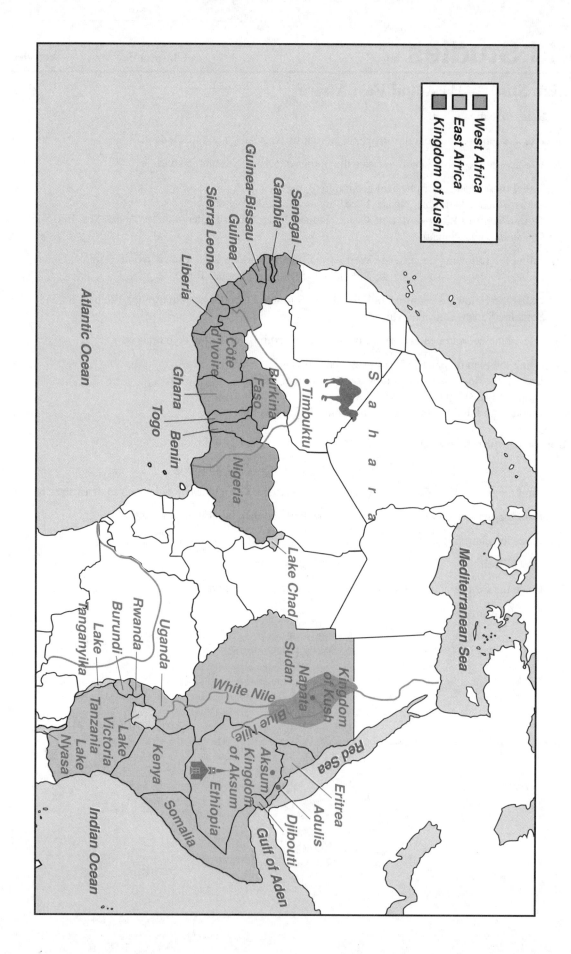

Legend:
- West Africa
- East Africa
- Kingdom of Kush

Atlantic Ocean

Senegal
Gambia
Guinea-Bissau
Guinea
Sierra Leone
Liberia
Côte d'Ivoire
Ghana
Togo
Benin
Burkina Faso
Nigeria
•Timbuktu
Sahara
Lake Chad
Mediterranean Sea

Uganda
Rwanda
Burundi
Lake Tanganyika
Lake Victoria
Tanzania
Lake Nyasa
Kenya
Somalia
Indian Ocean
Sudan
Napata
White Nile
Blue Nile
Kingdom of Kush
Red Sea
Aksum
Kingdom of Aksum
Adulis
Eritrea
Djibouti
Ethiopia
Gulf of Aden

World Studies

African Folktale

African folktales had many different purposes. Some explained things, while others taught moral lessons. They also teach us about the African way of life. The following West African folktale is called "Guinea Fowl and Rabbit Get Justice." Read the story and complete the questions at the end of each section.

Somewhere between the Kong Mountains and the sea, in the country of Ghana, the bird named Guinea Fowl had his farm. It was a good farm. Guinea Fowl worked hard on it, and grew fine yams and bananas. He grew beans and okra, millet and tobacco. His farm always looked green and prosperous. Mostly it was because Guinea Fowl was a hard worker. Not very far away Rabbit had a farm. It wasn't a very good farm because Rabbit never worked too hard. He planted at planting time, but he never hoed his crops or pulled out the weeds that grew there. So when harvest time came along there wasn't very much okra or beans or millet. One day Rabbit was out walking and he saw Guinea Fowl's farm. It looked so much better than his own that he wished he owned it. He thought it over. He became indignant.

"Why is it that it rains over here on Guinea Fowl's land and not on mine, so that his crops grow and mine don't?" he asked himself. "It's not fair!"

He thought all day. And a wonderful idea came to him.

That night he brought out his wife and his children and marched them to Guinea Fowl's farm, then he marched them back again. He did it again. All night his family went back and forth from their house to Guinea Fowl's farm, until by morning they had made a trail. In the morning they started pulling up Guinea Fowl's vegetables and putting them in baskets.

When Guinea Fowl came to work he saw Rabbit there with his family, pulling up all the fine crops he had planted.

"What are you doing with my yams and okra?" Guinea Fowl said. "And what are you doing on my farm, anyway?"

"*Your* farm?" Rabbit said. "There must be some mistake. It's *my* farm."

"I guess there *is* a mistake. It's my farm. I planted it and weeded it and hoed it," Guinea Fowl said. "So I don't see how it can be your farm."

"How could you plant it and weed it and hoe it when I planted it and weeded it and hoed it?" Rabbit said.

Guinea Fowl was very angry.

"You'd better get off my place," he said.

"You'd better get off *my* place," Rabbit said.

"It's absurd," Guinea Fowl said.

"It certainly is," Rabbit said, "when any old Guinea Fowl can come and claim someone else's property."

"It's mine," Guinea Fowl said.

"It's mine," Rabbit said.

"Well, I'll take the case to the chief," Guinea Fowl said.

So the two of them picked up their hoes and went to the village to the house of the chief.

"This fellow is pulling up my vegetables," Guinea Fowl said, "and he won't get off my farm."

"He's trying to take advantage of me," Rabbit said. "I work and work to grow fine yams and then he comes along and wants to own them."

They argued and argued, while the head man listened. Finally they went out together to look the situation over.

"Where is the trail from your house?" the head man asked Rabbit.

"There," Rabbit said, and pointed out the one he had just made.

"And where is the trail from your house?" the head man asked Guinea Fowl.

"Trail? I never had a trail," Guinea Fowl said.

"Whenever anyone has a farm he has a trail to it from his house," the head man said.

"But whenever I come to work my farm I *fly*," Guinea Fowl said.

The head man thought. He shook his head.

"If a person has a farm he has to have a trail to it," he said after a while. "So the land must belong to Rabbit."

He went away. Rabbit and his family began to pull up more yams. Guinea Fowl went home, feeling very angry.

1. Name the country this West African folktale comes from. Find the country on page 110 of your textbook and then list the three modern countries that surround it.   *Ghana; Burkina Faso, Cote d'Ivoire, and Togo*

2. Based on what you know about Guinea Fowl and Rabbit's farms, what types of products are traditionally grown in West Africa?   *yams, bananas, beans, okra, millet, and tobacco*

3. Why did Rabbit think Guinea Fowl's farm was better than his? What was the real reason for the difference?   *Rabbit thought it rained more on Guinea Fowl's land. Rabbit was lazy; he never hoed his crops or pulled up weeds.*

4. Why did Rabbit build a trail to Guinea Fowl's farm?   *He built the trail so it would look like he went there often and the farm belonged to him.*

5. To whom did Guinea Fowl and Rabbit take their problem? Was his judgment correct?   *the chief (or head man); no*

When Rabbit had a large basket full of vegetables he started off to market with them. But the basket was very heavy. He wasn't used to heavy work, because he was lazy. After he had carried his load a little distance along the road he put it down to rest. And while he sat by the roadside Guinea Fowl came along.

"Ah, friend Rabbit, your load is very heavy," Guinea Fowl said sweetly. "Perhaps I can give you a lift with it."

Rabbit was touched. Guinea Fowl wasn't angry anymore. He was very friendly.

"Thank you," he said. "You are a real friend to help me with my vegetables."

So Guinea Fowl put the load on his head. He smiled at Rabbit. Then he flapped his wings and went off with the load, not to the market but to his own house.

Rabbit shouted. He ran after Guinea Fowl, but he couldn't catch him. Guinea Fowl soared over the field and was gone.

Rabbit was angry. He went back to the village to find the head man.

"Guinea Fowl has robbed me!" he shouted. "He flew away with my basket of vegetables!"

The head man sent for Guinea Fowl.

"They were my vegetables I took," Guinea Fowl said.

"They were mine," Rabbit shouted. "I harvested them with my own hands!"

They argued and argued. The head man thought and thought.

"Well," he said at last, "when people carry things a great deal on their heads, after a while the hair gets thin from so much carrying." The people of the village said yes, that always happened.

"Let me see the top of your head," the head man said to Rabbit.

Rabbit showed him. The head man clicked his tongue.

"No," he said to Rabbit, "your hair is thick and long."

He turned to Guinea Fowl.

"Let me see yours," he said, and Guinea Fowl showed him.

Guinea Fowl's head didn't have even a fuzzy feather on it.

"It must belong to you," the head man said, "you are absolutely bald."

"But Guinea Fowl never *had* any feathers on his head!" Rabbit complained. "He was *always* bald!"

"When you carry things on your head the hair becomes thin," the head man said. "So the basket belongs to Guinea Fowl."

They went away. Rabbit prepared another basket of vegetables to take to market. And when he set it down by the side of the road to rest, Guinea Fowl swooped down and took it away. Rabbit prepared another basket, and the same thing happened. It was no use going to the head man any more, because Guinea Fowl's head was so bald.

At last Rabbit got tired of pulling up Guinea Fowl's vegetables for him, and he went back to his own farm to work for himself.

That is why people sometimes say, "The shortest path often goes nowhere."

6. Which of the two animals was trickier? _Answers will vary. Both animals were tricky. Rabbit made the trail to look like he owned the farm. Guinea Fowl acted like he was going to help Rabbit but instead flew off with the vegetables._

7. Based on the story, how did West African people traditionally bring their vegetables to market? _They carried the vegetables in baskets on their heads._

8. How did the chief decide who owned the basket of vegetables? _He looked at the tops of Guinea Fowl's and Rabbit's heads. The one with thinner hair had been carrying the basket._

9. Why did Rabbit go back to his own farm? _Guinea Fowl kept on taking the vegetables. Rabbit could not go back to the chief because a decision on the case had already been made._

10. Explain the saying at the end of the folktale in your own words. _Answers will vary. "The easiest way doesn't always work."_

World Studies

Chapter 5   **Activity E**

Geography Skills

Case #1:

At 2 A.M. Saturday the famous Regent diamond was stolen from the Louvre Museum in France. Police are holding the Graffi family robbers responsible for the crime. The ringleader, Giovanni, or "Geo," escaped with the diamond and has fled the country. However, his two nephews Carto and Topo were caught and arrested. On one of them, police found a list from Giovanni giving the nephews directions where to reunite with him.

This message has been handed over to the Geographic Intelligence Agency. The GIA has called upon its best agent, Sir Henry Vey, to follow the clues, track down Geo Graffi, and recover the diamond. Use the maps in the first five chapters and on pages 606-14 to solve the crime.

1. **"Starting in Paris, France, head toward the prime meridian."**

   Which cardinal direction must Vey travel to reach the line in the least amount of time? _west_

2. **"Follow the prime meridian south to a latitude of 20 degrees below the equator."**

   How many continents are found along this line? _three_

3. **"Travel along this latitude until you come to the continent that has a large portion of varied highland climate in the east. Head to these mountains."**

   Which of the three continents must Vey head to? _Africa_

   Which country do you think he will end up in? _Ethiopia_

4. **"From this point, head toward the tropic of Cancer."**

   Which cardinal direction does Vey head to reach the line? _north_

5. **"Once you reach this point, head east until you intersect with a longitude of 80 degrees east."**

   What country will Vey come to? _India_

   What climates are found in this country? _tropical wet, tropical wet and dry, tropical and temperate_

   dry, semiarid, humid subtropical, and varied highland

6. **"Head past the equator to a latitude of 90 degrees."**

   Is Sir Vey heading to the North or South Pole? _South Pole_

7. **"Travel to the location nearest this point where there is a marine west coast climate."**

   Which continent will Vey be in? _South America_

8. **"In this continent, head to the country that is found on the tropic of Capricorn and has no coastline. You'll find me in the capital city."**

   In what country and city will Vey find "Geo"? _Paraguay; Asunción_

World Studies

Chapter 6   Activity A

Exploring Time

Place the proper name and date(s) in the rows to match the events. After you have completed the chart, place the names and events on the time line.

Person	Date(s)	Events
Hernando Cortés	1519	arrives at Tenochtitlán
Bartolomeu Dias	1487	rounds the tip of Africa for first time
Vasco da Gama	1497	reaches India by Cape of Good Hope
Erik the Red	986	Greenland settled by Vikings
Leif Erikson	1003	Viking exploration of New World
Sir Francis Drake	1577-80	sails around world for England
Ferdinand Magellan	1519-22	his crew is first to sail around world
Marco Polo	1271-95	in the Far East during time of Kublai Khan
Francisco Pizarro	1532	overthrows Inca Empire
Christopher Columbus	1492	discovers New World for Spain
Francis Xavier	1549	arrives in Japan

People
Bartolomeu Dias
Christopher Columbus
Erik the Red
Ferdinand Magellan
Francis Xavier
Francisco Pizarro
Hernando Cortés
Leif Erikson
Marco Polo
Sir Francis Drake
Vasco da Gama

Date(s)
986
1003
1271-95
1487
1492
1497
1519
1519-22
1532
1549
1577-80

900	Time Line
1000	*986: Erik the Red—settles Greenland*
	1003: Leif Erikson—explores New World
1100	
1200	
1300	*1271-95: Marco Polo—in the Far East*
1400	
1500	*1487: Bartolomeu Dias—rounds tip of Africa* *1492: Christopher Columbus—discovers New World* *1497: Vasco da Gama—reaches India*
	1519: Hernando Cortés—arrives at Tenochtitlán *1519-22: Ferdinand Magellan—crew circles world* *1532: Francisco Pizarro—overthrows Incas* *1549: Francis Xavier—arrives in Japan*
1600	*1577-80: Sir Francis Drake—sails around the world*

World Studies

Chapter 6   Activity B

Keyword Clues

This game is called "Keyword Clues." For each of the terms, write three one-word clues *without using any portion of the term*. Give one clue at a time until your partner comes up with the term. Each clue adds a point to the person's score. The team that needs the fewest clues and has the lowest score, wins. (If your partner misses the term after three clues, give him the answer and count it as the fourth "clue.") *Adapt this activity to your class, but make the rules clear.*

Score	Term	First Clue	Second Clue	Third Clue
	People			
	Prince Henry	Portuguese	royalty	exploration
	Erik the Red			
	Ferdinand Magellan			
	Bartolomeu Dias			
	King Ferdinand			
	Mayas			
	Vasco da Gama			
	Francis Xavier			
	Queen Isabella			
	Montezuma			
	Leif Erikson			
	samurai			
	Sir Francis Drake			
	Francisco Pizarro			
	Hernando Cortés			
	Aztecs			
	skraelings			
	shoguns			
	Vikings			
	Christopher Columbus			
	Places			
	Cuzco			
	Tenochititlán			
	Cape of Storms			

Score		First Clue	Second Clue	Third Clue
	Greenland			
	Teotihuacán			
	Japan			
	doldrums			
	horse latitudes			
	Things			
	compass			
	seppuku			
	caravel			
	astrolabe			
	trade winds			
	dead reckoning			

World Studies

Chapter 6   Activity C

Map Study—Middle America

Refer to text pages 148 and 150.

1. **Label** Mexico and use a colored pencil to **shade** it blue.

2. **Label** Central America and use a colored pencil to **shade** those countries included in it green.

3. **Circle** the three island groups in the Caribbean Sea using a different colored pencil for each. **Label** all three groups.

4. **Label** the following features of physical geography:
   Bodies of Water—Atlantic Ocean, Caribbean Sea, Gulf of California, Gulf of Honduras, Gulf of Mexico, Lake Nicaragua, Pacific Ocean
   Miscellaneous—Panama Canal

5. **Label** the following countries:
   Belize, Costa Rica, Cuba, El Salvador, Guatemala, Honduras, Nicaragua, Panama

6. **Label** the Aztec Empire and use a colored pencil to **trace** its borders in purple.

7. **Label** the Mayan Empire and use a colored pencil to **trace** its borders in brown.

8. **Locate** and **label** Mexico City and then **place** the soldier icon next to it to show the influence of Hernando Cortés.

 Soldier

World Studies

Map Study—World Exploration

Follow the directions below to complete the map.

1. Using the map on page 134:
   With a blue colored pencil, **draw** arrows to show the trade winds above and below the equator. **Label** both of them.

2. Using the map on page 138:
   Circle the Portuguese bases on the west coast of Africa.

3. Using the maps on pages 139 and 142:
   With different colored pencils for each, **draw** the routes of the following explorers and complete the key at the bottom of the map: Christopher Columbus, Bartolomeu Dias, Francis Drake, Vasco da Gama, Ferdinand Magellan. Use the key on page 142 as an example.

4. Using the map on page 148:
   Label the Incan empire and use a colored pencil to **shade** it green.

Optional

5. **Place** the missionary icon next to the country Francis Xavier described as the "Country at War."

6. **Place** the explorer icon on the land discovered by Erik the Red.

    Missionary

   Explorer

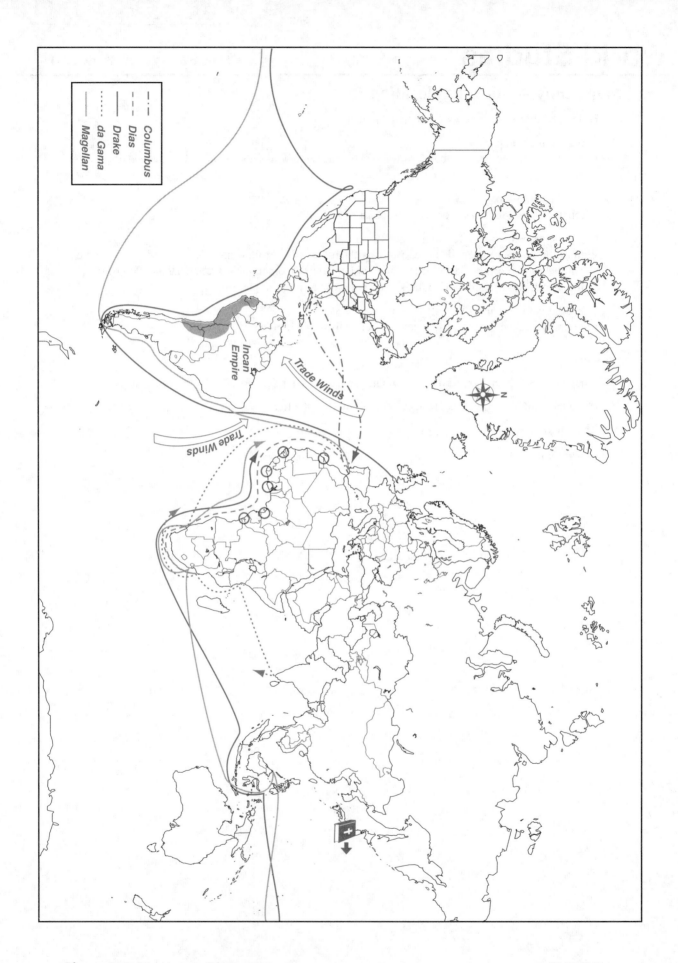

Legend:
- Columbus
- Dias
- Drake
- da Gama
- Magellan

Incan Empire

Trade Winds

Trade Winds

N

World Studies

Christopher Columbus

Read the entries from Columbus's journal and answer the questions that follow. *Students may work in a group to answer the questions.*

Friday, 3 August

We set sail on Friday, 3 August 1492, crossing the bar of the Saltés at eight o'clock. Sailed S with a strong, veering wind until sunset, making forty-eight miles, or sixteen leagues; then SW and S by W, on course for the Canaries.

Sunday, 9 September

We sailed sixteen and a half leagues. I have decided to log less than our true run, so that if the voyage is long the crew will not be afraid and lose heart.

Sunday, 16 September

The voyage is growing long, and we are far from home, and the men are beginning to complain about the length of the journey and about me for involving them in it. When they saw these great rafts of weed in the distance they began to be afraid that there were rocks or submerged ground, which made them even more impatient and outspoken in their complaints against me. Having seen the ships sailing through the weed, however, they have lost their fear somewhat, though not entirely.

Tuesday, 25 September

At sunset Martín Alonso went up on the poop of his ship and called to me full of happiness with the good news that he could see land. When he repeated it and said it was definite, I knelt down to give thanks to God. Martín Alonso was saying the *Gloria in excelsis Deo* with his people, and mine did the same. The crew on the Niña all climbed up the mast and into the rigging, and all agreed that it was land.

Wednesday, 26 September

Sailed on course W until after noon, then SW until we found that what we had thought to be land was only clouds. Our twenty-four hour run was about thirty-three leagues; I told the men twenty-five and a half. The sea was just like a river, with sweet, gentle breezes.

Saturday, 6 October

Remained on course W. Forty-two and a half leagues in the twenty-four hours; I told the men thirty-five. Martín Alonso said tonight that we would be best to steer SW by W. I think he had the island of Cipangu in mind when he said this. My own opinion is that if we miss Cipangu we shall be a long time in making landfall, and it is better to strike the mainland first and go to the islands afterwards.

Wednesday, 10 October

Sailed WSW at about eight knots, sometimes up to nine and a half, occasionally only five and a half. Sixty-two and a half leagues in the twenty-four hours; I told the men only forty-six and a half. They could contain themselves no longer, and began to complain of the length of the voyage. I encouraged them as best I could, trying to raise their hopes of the benefits they might gain from it. I also told them that it was useless to complain; having set out for the Indies I shall continue this voyage until, with God's grace, I reach them.

Thursday, 11 October

Course WSW. A heavy sea, the roughest in the whole voyage so far. We saw petrels, and a green reed close to the ship, and then a big green fish of a kind which does not stray far from the shoals. On the Pinta they saw a cane and a stick, and they picked up another little piece of wood which seemed to have been worked with an iron tool; also a piece of cane and another plant which grows on land, and a thorn-branch laden with red fruits, apparently newly cut. We were all filled with joy and relief at these signs. Sailed twenty-eight and a half leagues before sunset. After sunset I resumed our original course westward, sailing about nine knots. By two o'clock in the morning we had sailed about sixty-eight miles, or twenty-two and a half leagues.

I was on the poop deck at ten o'clock in the evening when I saw a light. It was so indistinct that I could not be sure it was land, but I called Pedro Gutiérrez, the Butler of the King's Table, and I told him to look at what I thought was a light. He looked, and saw it. I also told Rodrigo Sánchez de Segovia, Your Majesties' observer on board, but he saw nothing because he was standing in the wrong place. After I had told them, the light appeared once or twice more, like a wax candle rising and falling. Only a few people thought it was a sign of land, but I was sure we were close to landfall.

Then the Pinta, being faster and in the lead, sighted land and made the signal as I ordered. The first man to sight land was called Rodrigo de Triana. The land appeared two hours after midnight, about two leagues away. . . .

When we stepped ashore we saw green trees, streams everywhere and different kinds of fruit. I called to the two captains to jump ashore with the rest, who included Rodrigo de Escobedo, secretary of the fleet, and Rodrigo Sánchez de Segovia, asking them to bear witness that in the presence of them all I was taking possession of this island for their Lord and Lady the King and Queen, and I made the necessary declarations which are set down at greater length in the written testimonies.

Soon many islanders gathered round us. I could see that they were people who would be more easily converted to our Holy Faith by love than by coercion, and wishing them to look on us with friendship I gave some of them red bonnets and glass beads which they hung round their necks, and many other things of small value, at which they were so delighted and so eager to please us that we could not believe it. Later they swam out to the boats to bring us parrots and balls of thread and darts, and many other things, exchanging them for such objects as glass beads and hawk bells. They took anything, and gave willingly whatever they had.

Discussion Questions

1. What did Columbus do to keep his men from complaining? _Columbus logged less distance than he had actually traveled so his men wouldn't think they were that far from home. He also tried to encourage them by reminding them of the benefits they might receive from the voyage, and he told them of his own determination to succeed._

2. Why were the men afraid of the weeds on the ocean? _Answers may vary. They thought there were rocks underneath them that would sink the ship._

3. Who was the captain of the Pinta? _Martín Alonso_

4. What did the land that Martín Alonso saw turn out to be? _clouds_

5. What signs showed Columbus and his men that they were close to land? _Birds, plants, and certain fish all indicated that land was near. They also saw a piece of wood that appeared to have been worked with a tool. In the evening, Columbus saw a light that he believed indicated land nearby._

6. What day did Columbus and his men experience the roughest weather? _Thursday, 11 October_

7. What was the name of the first man to sight land? _Rodrigo de Triana_

8. For whom did Columbus take possession of the island? (be specific) _King Ferdinand and Queen Isabella of Spain._

9. Why did Columbus give the islanders gifts? _He wanted to show them friendship and eventually see them converted to Roman Catholicism._

10. In which ship was Columbus sailing? _Santa Maria_

Optional

11. Find on a map the Canary Islands mentioned on August 3rd. What continent are the islands closest to? _Africa_

12. What do you think the *Gloria in excelsis Deo* was that Alonso said with his crew? _Answers may vary. Spain was Catholic, so this was probably a Catholic prayer. (means "glory to God in the highest")_

13. Both Columbus and Alonso thought they were near the island of Cipangu. What is the modern name of this country? _Japan_

14. How many days had the voyage lasted when land was finally sighted? (Hint: You'll need a calendar.) _69 days_

15. What do you think the light was that Columbus saw on the evening of October 11? _Answers will vary._

Skill: Original Sources

World Studies

Which Country?

Match the following people, places, or events with the correct country. Some answers will be used more than once, and some will not be used.

Matching

A. Argentina   H. Suriname
B. Brazil   I. Bolivia
C. Chile   J. Colombia
D. Ecuador   K. Paraguay
E. Venezuela   L. Uruguay
F. French Guiana   M. Peru
G. Guyana

_____E_____ 1. the birthplace of Simón Bolívar

____B, J____ 2. most coffee grown

_____M_____ 3. San Martín and Bolívar brought independence here

_____E_____ 4. where the battle of Carabobo was fought

_____A_____ 5. home of the gauchos

_____B_____ 6. first emperor was Pedro I

_____L_____ 7. Treaty of San Ildefonso

_____H_____ 8. Dutch Guiana

_____B_____ 9. the home of O Aleijadinho

_____G_____ 10. British Guiana

_____F_____ 11. French settlement

_____B_____ 12. Thomé de Souza

_____A_____ 13. the Pampas

_____C_____ 14. Atacama Desert

_____J_____ 15. where the battle of Boyacá was fought

World Studies

Bolívar and Martín

Check the appropriate box for each statement. Some statements may apply to both leaders.

Bolívar	San Martín	
✔	✔	helped to bring independence to Peru
	✔	came from a prominent Argentine family
✔		sent as an ambassador to England
✔		greatest victories came at Boyacá and Carabobo
✔	✔	leader in the South American independence movement
	✔	used gauchos as his troops
✔		known as "the Liberator"
	✔	studied the strategies of his heroes
✔		pushed the Spaniards out of Venezuela
✔		died shortly after General Sucre was assassinated

Name _____

World Studies

Chapter 7　　　　Activity C

Map Study—South America

Refer to text pages 166 and 180.

1. Use colored pencils to **shade** the four regions of South America in different colors. **Create** a map key to go along with the regions.

2. **Label** these features of physical geography:
   Bodies of Water—Atlantic Ocean, Caribbean Sea, Pacific Ocean
   Miscellaneous—Amazon River, Andes Mountains, Atacama Desert, Pampas

3. **Label** the following countries:
   Argentina, Bolivia, Brazil, Chile, Colombia, Ecuador, French Guiana, Guyana, Paraguay, Peru, Suriname, Uruguay, Venezuela

4. **Locate** and **label** the cities of Bogota, Lima, and Santiago.
   Use colored pencils to **draw** and **label** the routes of Bolívar and San Martín. Use a different color for each.

Using Additional Resources—

Use an atlas, encyclopedia, or other resources to complete the following.

5. **Draw** and **label** the Line of Demarcation and the line established by the Treaty of Tordesillas.

6. Bolívar's greatest victories took place at Boyacá, Colombia, and at Carabobo, Venezuela. **Find** these sites and **place** the battle icon there. Hint: Both Boyacá and Carabobo are states within their countries. Tunja is the capital of Boyacá and Valencia is the capital of Carabobo.

   ✗ Battle

Reinforcement: Sections 1-2　　　　　　*Skill: Maps*　　**51**

Atlantic Ocean

Caribbean Sea

Guyana

Suriname

French
Guiana

Venezuela

Bogota
Colombia

Ecuador

Amazon R.

Bolívar

Peru

Brazil

Lima

Treaty of Tordesillas

Line of Demarcation

Pacific Ocean

Andes Mountains

Bolivia

Atacama Desert

Paraguay

San Martín

Chile

Argentina

Santiago

Uruguay

Pampas

Caribbean Republics
Andean Republics
River Plate Republics
Brazil

World Studies

Chapter 7   **Activity D**

Word Search

Fill in each blank with the appropriate word. Find each of these words in the word search.

creole	1.	a person of pure Spanish or Portuguese descent born in the Americas
degredado	2.	an undesirable citizen or convict of Portugal
barrio	3.	a Spanish neighborhood
hacienda	4.	a huge country estate
hacendado	5.	the owner of a Spanish estate
gaucho	6.	a cowboy of Argentina
bombacha	7.	the baggy pants worn by Argentine cowboys
caudillo	8.	a Latin American strong man
donatario	9.	the ruler of a captaincy in Brazil
audiencia	10.	a division of a Spanish territory administered by a Spanish lawyer
encomienda	11.	an estate or property awarded to a conquistador
mestizo	12.	a person with Indian and Spanish parents
peninsulare	13.	a Spaniard born in Spain
boleodoro	14.	three rocks tied to rawhide strips

World Studies

Exploring Explorers

Fill in the blanks on the following explorers using the information in your text.

Explorer	Home Country	Area Explored	Year(s) of Exploration	Reasons for Exploration	Results of Exploration
Hernando de Soto	Spanish	*Florida, Alabama, northern Mississippi, Arkansas*	*1539-42*	*to settle and to find gold*	*Many of the men, including de Soto, died during the expedition.*
Jacques Cartier	*French*	*along the Gulf of St. Lawrence and the St. Lawrence River*	*1534*	*to discover "isles and countries" and to find gold and riches*	*The French settled the area and established Montreal.*
Juan de Oñate	*Spanish*	*New Mexico*	*1597*	*to pacify the Indians and convert them to Catholicism*	*The Spanish established a temporary settlement at Española.*
Juan Ponce de León	*Spanish*	*Florida*	1513	*to discover new lands and to find the Fountain of Youth*	*After repeated Indian attacks, Ponce de León gave up exploring.*
Pánfilo de Narváez	*Spanish*	*Florida*	*1528*	*to explore and govern Florida*	*Many of the men died or were made Indian servants after their boats were destroyed in rough waters.*
Pedro Menéndez de Avilé	*Spanish*	Florida	*1535*	*to settle Florida before the French did*	*The French were chased away, and St. Augustine was founded.*
Samuel de Champlain	*French*	*around the St. Lawrence River and the Great Lakes*	*1608*	*to settle New France and make it self-supporting*	By Champlain's death in 1635, his colony was firmly established in Canada.
Sir Walter Raleigh	*English*	*Roanoke, North Carolina*	*1587*	to settle North America for the English	*The colonists disappeared mysteriously.*

World Studies

Early English Settlers

For each statement, decide whether it refers to the Pilgrims, Puritans, or Virginia Company. Place your answer in the blanks.

Puritans	1.	They believed their settlement was a "city that is set on a hill."
Puritans	2.	They were Anglicans who disagreed with certain church practices.
Pilgrims	3.	They settled at Plymouth, Massachusetts.
Virginia Company	4.	One of their colonists married an Indian chief's daughter named Pocahontas.
Pilgrims	5.	Their governor, William Bradford, wrote the history of the colony in his book.
Puritans	6.	They began their settlement in 1630.
Virginia Company	7.	Many settlers died of starvation and Indian attacks in their settlement called Jamestown.
Puritans	8.	Their settlement was known as the Massachusetts Bay Colony.
Virginia Company	9.	Their winter of 1609-10 was known as the "starving time."
Pilgrims	10.	They came to America in 1620 to avoid religious persecution.

Discussion Questions

11. How were the English settlements different from French and Spanish settlements? _Answers will vary._

    Unlike Spanish and French settlements, the English settlements were under private investors. Spanish and French settlers tended to be soldiers without their families. In contrast, English settlers usually came as families. Most Spanish and French settlers were Catholic, while the English tended to be Protestants.

12. How did education differ between the English and French settlements? _English settlers, especially those in Massachusetts, believed education was important in order to read and understand Scripture. Parents were held responsible for the early education of their children. Schools and colleges were soon built as towns grew. French settlements placed less emphasis on education. The Roman Catholic Church saw education as unnecessary for most. Scripture was not to be read by those outside the church._

13. Why did many of the Pilgrims' and Puritans' children turn away from their beliefs? _Although the children had been kept in a sheltered environment, sin was still in them as part of their nature. Without a personal relationship with God, they followed their worldly lusts and desires. Many of them had not experienced the persecutions their parents had endured back in England._

World Studies

Map Study—Canada

Refer to text pages 197 and 216.

1. **Label** these features of physical geography:
   Open Bodies of Water—Arctic Ocean, Atlantic Ocean, Baffin Bay, Beaufort Sea, Gulf of St. Lawrence, Hudson Bay, Labrador Sea, Pacific Ocean
   Lakes—Great Bear Lake, Great Slave Lake, Lake Athabasca, Lake Huron, Lake Michigan, Lake Nipigan, Lake Ontario, Lake Superior, Lake Winnipeg
   Miscellaneous—Great Plains, Rocky Mountains, St. Lawrence River

2. **Label** the following provinces and territories:
   Alberta, British Columbia, Manitoba, New Brunswick, Newfoundland, Northwest Territories, Nunavut, Nova Scotia, Ontario, Prince Edward Island, Quebec, Saskatchewan, Yukon Territory

3. Which province has a population that is 80 percent French? **Place** the French icon inside this province.
   (F) French

4. **Label** the Arctic Circle within Canada

5. With a colored pencil **shade** green the part of Canada where the early English and French fishermen came to fish.

Using Additional Resources—

Use an atlas, encyclopedia, or other resources to complete the following.

6. Use a blue colored pencil to **draw** and **label** the route of the Mackenzie River in Canada.

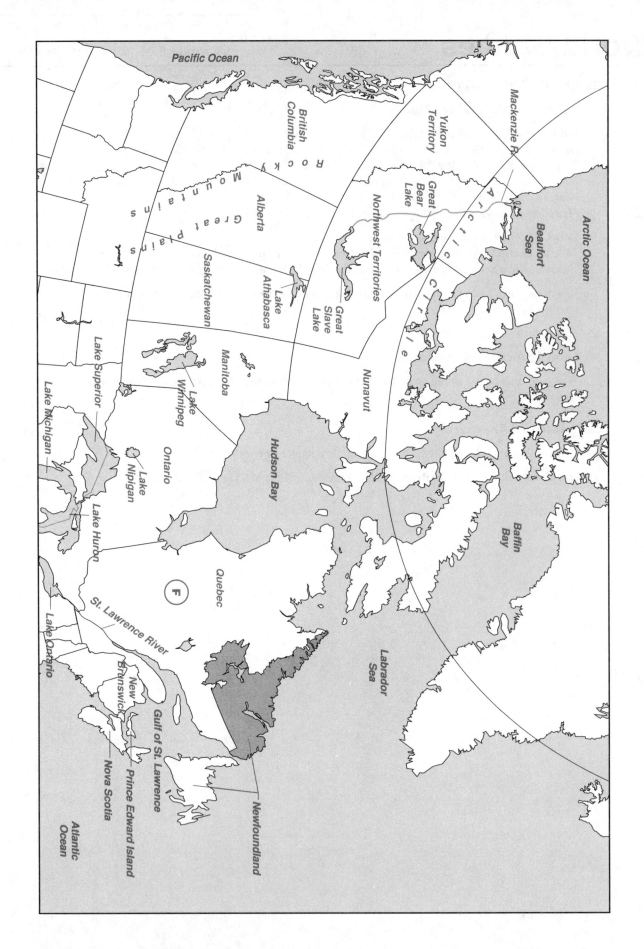

World Studies

Map Study—North America

Refer to text pages 188, 193, 194, and 199.

1. Use different colored pencils to **shade** the parts of North America settled by the French, English, and Spanish. **Create** a key to go along with the map.

2. **Draw** the routes of Ponce de León, Narváez, de Vaca, and de Soto. Use a different colored pencil for each route and then **label** each of them with the name of the appropriate explorer.

3. **Locate** and **label** the settlements at Montreal and Quebec. **Place** the French and explorer icons by both of these sites.

   (F) French

   �֍ Explorer

4. **Locate** and **label** San Francisco and San Diego. **Place** the mission icon by both of these sites.

   📖➤ Mission

Using Additional Resources—

Use an atlas, encyclopedia, or other resources to complete the following.

5. **Find** the modern city of St. Augustine located in Florida and then **locate** and **label** it on your map. **Place** the Spanish icon next to the site.

   (s) Spanish

6. **Find** Gaspé Bay (or Gaspé Peninsula) in Canada. **Place** the French and explorer icons there to show Cartier's first visit.

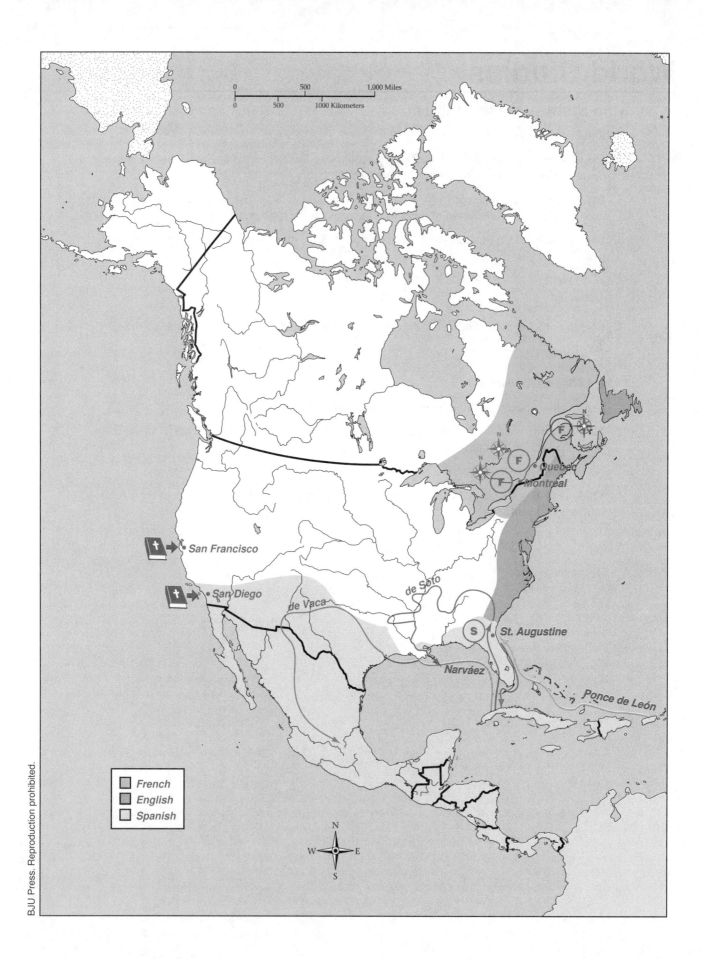

French

English

Spanish

San Francisco

San Diego

de Vaca

de Soto

Narváez

St. Augustine

Ponce de León

Quebec

Montreal

N
W — E
S

World Studies

Chapter 8   **Activity E**

Map Study—United States Expansion

Refer to text pages 200 and 211.

1. **Locate** and **label** the following settlements—Jamestown, Plymouth, Roanoke Island.

2. **Label** the part of the United States known as the original thirteen states. Use a colored pencil to **shade** the area green.

3. Use a yellow colored pencil to **shade** those parts of the United States that were purchased from another country. **Label** each area and **place** in each the proper icon that corresponds to the country from which it was purchased.

   F French

   M Mexican

   R Russia

4. Use a red colored pencil to **shade** the portion of the United States that was ceded by Spain. **Label** the area and **place** the Spanish icon there.

   S Spanish

5. Use a blue colored pencil to **shade** those parts of the United States that were acquired in the 1840s. **Label** each of these areas.

6. **Label** these features of physical geography:
   Bodies of Water—Atlantic Ocean, Gulf of Mexico, Pacific Ocean
   Rivers—Colorado River, Mississippi River, Missouri River
   Islands—Aleutian Islands, Hawaiian Islands

Using Additional Resources—

Use an atlas, encyclopedia, or other resources to complete the following.

7. **Place** the school icon within or next to the states in which these universities are found:
   Dartmouth, Harvard, Princeton, Rutgers, William and Mary, Yale.

    School

8. Look at the line that divided the original thirteen states from the rest of the country. **Find** and **label** the major physical feature found along this line.

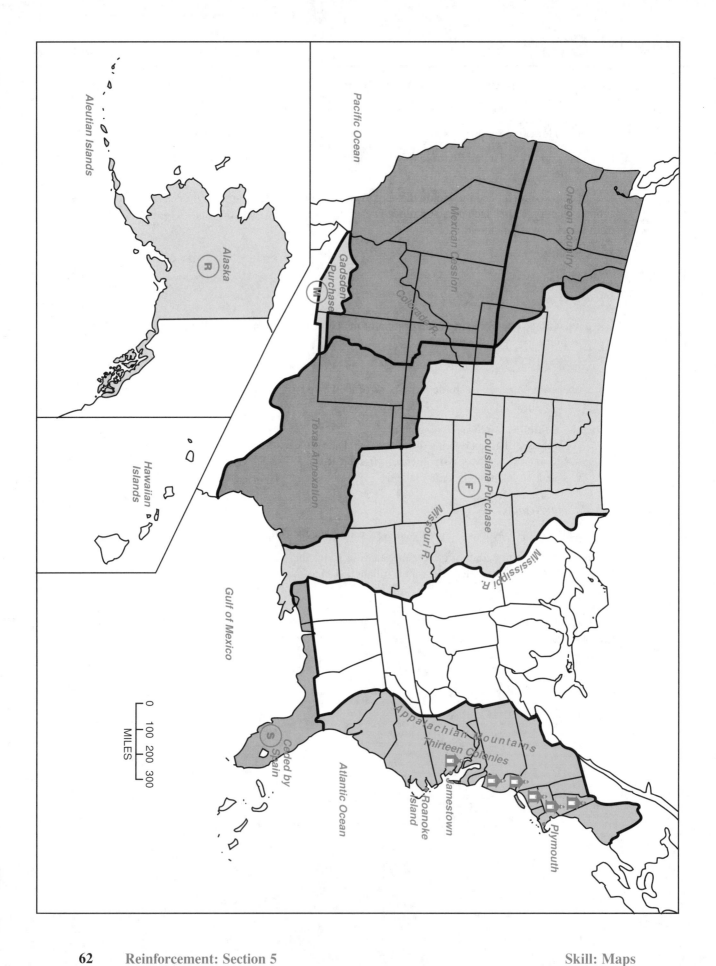

World Studies

Survival

Early settlers to the New World faced an uphill battle to start a colony. Begin a colony with 250 settlers. Make a spinner like the one shown and move the settlement through the board. See how many settlers are left by the time you reach the end. (Having no settlers is a possible result.) Compare your settlement results with those of your classmates. *The majority of spaces on the board are unfavorable in order to simulate the low survival rate of early settlers in the first few years.*

On a separate sheet of paper, copy or trace the circle, arrow, and game piece below. Do NOT cut out the examples. When you have the pieces copied, cut them out. Using the end of your pencil, punch a small hole in the center of the circle. Tape the arrow to a flat surface. Place the circle slightly under the arrow as shown in the illustration. Place the tip of your pencil in the punched hole and spin the spinner. Use the game piece to mark your place as you proceed around the board.

If you plan to use the game as a class activity, copy one spinner for each group of four or five students. Use heavyweight paper such as poster board or manila folders. Copy enough game pieces for your entire class. Give these pieces to the students prior to playing the game so that they can color them for easy identification.

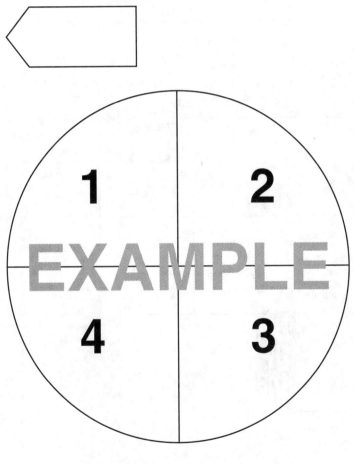

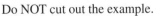

Do NOT cut out the example.

A storm sinks one of the ships. Fifty settlers are lost.	Four settlers die from sickness on the voyage.	Half of the settlement's provisions are spoiled during the voyage. Thirteen die from starvation.	Only a few settlers are skilled workers. Twenty-one settlers die from starvation.	Little food and poor nutrition leads to scurvy. Thirty-nine settlers die from it.	A recent plague has lowered the Indian population. The settlers are able to use the dwellings and cleared fields.	The settlement is in a swampy area. Fifteen settlers die from malaria.

Five settlers die from dysentery.

FIRST WINTER One-half of the settlers die from sickness, starvation, and the cold.

FIRST WINTER One-half of the settlers die from sickness, starvation, and the cold.

The settlement has arrived too close to winter to plant crops. One-fourth of the settlers die from starvation.

Forty-five settlers die in an ambush by Indians.

A supply ship arrives, but all of the settlers have disappeared mysteriously. GAME OVER

Thirty-two settlers desert the settlement to try to return to England.

Hastily built structures provide little defense from the weather. Seven settlers die from exposure.

A supply ship arrives with food and one hundred new settlers.

A deadly fever spreads through the settlement. Twenty-five settlers die.

Investors back in England lose interest in the settlement. One-third of the settlers leave.

A disease is spread through foul drinking water. Sixteen settlers die.

A drought in the area makes food scarce. Six die of starvation.

War in Europe cuts off supplies to the settlers. The settlement is abandoned. GAME OVER

Friendly Indians provide food and shelter.

Five are captured by Indians and made servants.

A ship headed for England visits the settlement. Fifteen settlers catch a ride on it.

A cash crop is discovered. Investors see profit and send over one hundred new settlers.

SECOND WINTER One-third of the settlers die.

SECOND WINTER One-third of the settlers die.

A fire destroys many of the settlement's structures. Nine die during the winter months.

A group of settlers gets lost in a storm. Seven settlers disappear.

Some of the crops are destroyed by hostile Indians. Twelve settlers die of starvation and illness.

Eleven babies are born, but four die in infancy. Three mothers also die in childbirth.

Three settlers are attacked by wild animals and killed.

In an effort to wipe out the settlement, an Indian chief organizes an attack. One hundred of the settlers are killed.

Survivors from another settlement arrive. Add twenty-five settlers to the settlement.

Congratulations! The settlement has made it through the crucial first years. Calculate how many settlers are left and compare the results with other classmates.

World Studies

Chapter 8   **Activity G**

Transcontinental Trivia

Using additional resources, find the answers to as many of these trivia questions as possible.

1. On what day was the last spike driven in to complete the Transcontinental Railroad?   *May 10, 1869*

2. Who drove in the last spike to complete the railroad? Why was he important?   *Leland Stanford; he*
    was the president of the Central Pacific Railroad

3. What were the names of the two railroad companies that completed the Transcontinental Railroad?
    Central Pacific Railroad and Union Pacific Railroad

4. Work on the Transcontinental Railroad began in 1862. Who was the president of the United States at
    that time?   *Abraham Lincoln*

5. Who was president at its completion in 1869?   *Ulysses Grant*

6. How many states were there in 1869? Was Utah one of them?   *thirty-seven; no*

7. What war disrupted the construction of the railroad?   *the Civil War*

8. Extra Credit: What was the telegraph message sent from coast to coast upon completion of the
    railroad?   *"Done"*

9. Who was the prime minister of Canada when the Canadian Pacific Railroad was completed?
    Sir John A. MacDonald

10. How many provinces were part of Canada at that time?   *seven*

11. How many years had Canada been a nation when the Canadian Pacific Railroad was completed?
    twenty-four

World Studies

Chapter 9   **Activity A**

Watts and Wesley

Isaac Watts and Charles Wesley were some of the greatest hymn writers the church has ever known. Use one or more hymnals to find information on them and their works.

Isaac Watts

year of birth: *1674* _____

year of death: *1748* _____

Hymnal(s) used in search: *Answers will vary.* _____

Total number of hymns written: *Answers will vary. Watts wrote around 600 hymns during his lifetime.*

Choose one of his hymns and explain the theme. *Answers will vary. Some examples include "Alas! and Did My Saviour Bleed?" "Marching to Zion," and "When I Survey the Wondrous Cross."*

Choose one verse from the hymn and explain its meaning. *Answers will vary.* _____

_____

_____

_____

Find three verses of Scripture that relate to this hymn. Write the verses and their references here. (Some hymns are based directly on a passage of Scripture.)

   reference and verse _____

_____

   reference and verse _____

_____

   reference and verse _____

_____

Charles Wesley

year of birth: *1707* _____

year of death: *1788* _____

Hymnal(s) used in search: *Answers will vary.* _____

Total number of hymns written: *Answers will vary. Wesley wrote around 6000 hymns during his lifetime.*

Choose one of his hymns and explain the theme. *Answers will vary. Some examples include "And Can It Be That I Should Gain?" "O for a Thousand Tongues to Sing," and "Soldiers of Christ, Arise."*

Choose one verse from the hymn and explain its meaning.   *Answers will vary.*

_____

_____

_____

_____

Find three verses of Scripture that relate to this hymn. Write the verses and their references here. (Some hymns are based directly on a passage of Scripture.)

   reference and verse
_____

_____

   reference and verse
_____

_____

   reference and verse
_____

_____

Composers

   Both Franz Josef Haydn and Wolfgang Amadeus Mozart wrote music to which hymn texts have been set. Write below as many hymns as you can find composed by either Hadyn or Mozart.

Franz Josef Haydn   *Answers include "The Spacious Firmament," "Glorious Things of Thee Are Spoken," and*

"Standing at the Portal."

_____

Wolfgang Amadeus Mozart   *Answers include "O Could I Speak the Matchless Worth," "Jesus, I My Cross*

Have Taken," and "Hark, the Voice of Jesus Calling."

_____

World Studies

Chapter 9   **Activity B**

Search the Facts

In each of the rows, one term does not fit. Underline the term and write the correct answer below it. In the last category, **Event/Description/Accomplishment,** more than one answer may be correct.

Person	Country	Date(s)	Event/Description/Accomplishment
Maria Theresa	Austria	<u>1680-1723</u> *1740-80*	improved conditions for the peasants
Peter the Great	<u>Prussia</u> *Russia*	1682-1725	traveled to learn trades and meet monarchs
<u>Isaac Newton</u> *John Wesley*	England	1762-96	formed the Methodist Church
Napoleon	<u>Austria</u> *France*	1804	became dictator
<u>Charles I</u> *Frederick the Great*	Prussia	1740-86	built up the army and added territory to the kingdom
Louis XVI	France	1774-92	<u>the Sun King</u> *Answers may vary. He was ruler when the French Revolution began.*
Franz Joseph Haydn	Austria	1732-1809	<u>Enlightenment philosopher</u> *Answers may vary. He was a classical composer who performed in Maria Theresa's court.*
Robert Raikes	<u>United States</u> *England*	1780	opened the first Sunday school
Wolfgang Amadeus Mozart	Austria	<u>1756-95</u> *1756-91*	classical composer who performed in Maria Theresa's court
Catherine the Great	Russia	1762-96	<u>made her capital the center of European classical music</u> *Answers may vary. She added land to Russia, including part of Poland.*
Louis XIV	France	<u>1598</u> *1685*	revoked the Edict of Nantes
<u>King John</u> *William and Mary*	England	1688	accepted the English Bill of Rights
<u>Isaac Watts</u> *James Watt*	Scotland	1769	patented his steam engine

World Studies

Map Study—Eastern Europe

Refer to text pages 234 and 610.

1. **Label** the following countries:
   Belarus, Czech Republic, Estonia, Hungary, Latvia, Lithuania, Poland, Slovakia, Ukraine

2. **Label** the following cities:
   Bratislava, Budapest, Kiev, Minsk, Prague, Riga, Tallinn, Vilnius, Warsaw

3. **Label** these features of physical geography:
   Bodies of Water—Baltic Sea, Black Sea, Gulf of Finland, North Sea, Sea of Azov
   Rivers—Danube River, Dnieper River
   Miscellaneous—Carpathian Mountains, Crimean Peninsula

4. Using the map of Europe on page 610 of your text, complete the following:
   Use a blue colored pencil to **draw** and **label** these rivers in Eastern Europe—Dniester River, Oder River, Vistula River
   Label the Baltic Plains

Using Additional Resources—

Use an atlas, encyclopedia, or other resources to complete the following.

5. General Casimir Pulaski served in the American Revolutionary War on the side of the patriots. **Find** the country he was from and **place** the soldier icon within it.

   † Soldier

6. In 1986 there was a terrible nuclear disaster at Chernobyl in the Ukraine. **Find** this site and then **locate** and **label** it on your map.

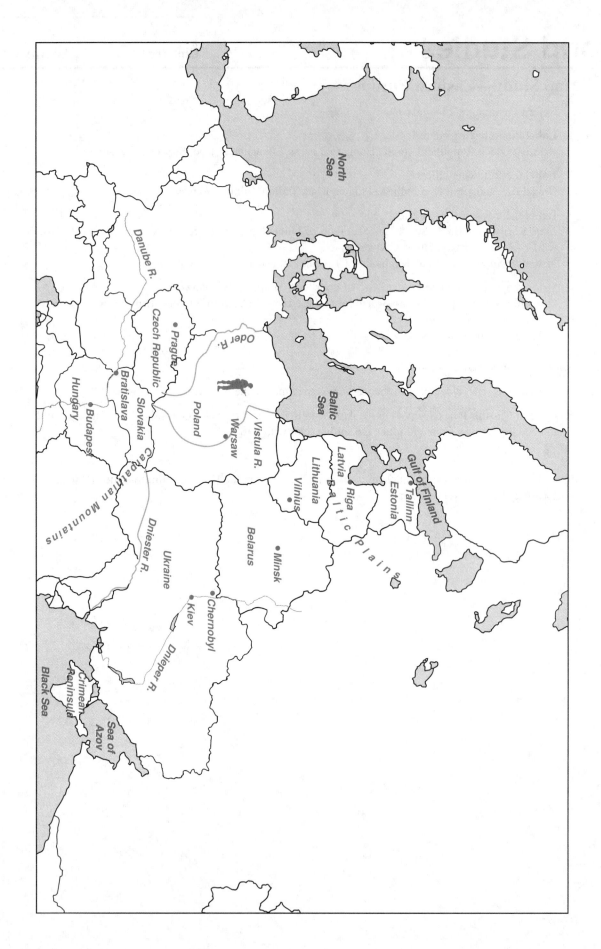

World Studies

Map Study—Europe in 1763

Refer to text pages 225, 232, and 238.

1. **Label** the following area and use different colored pencils to **shade** each of them:
   Austria, Britain, France, Prussia, Russia, Spain

2. **Label** these cities within Europe:
   Berlin, Constantinople, London, Paris, Rome, St. Petersburg, Vienna, Warsaw

3. **Label** these bodies of water:
   Atlantic Ocean, Baltic Sea, Black Sea, Mediterranean Sea, North Sea

4. Read the list of philosophers in the first paragraph on page 238. **Place** the philosopher icon in the proper country or area where each philosopher was from.

   Philosopher

5. **Place** the composer icon next to the city where Haydn and Mozart both performed.

   Composer

6. **Locate** and **label** the cities of Calais, Dijon, Genoa, Florence, London, Lyons, Marseilles, Rome, and Venice. You may need outside sources to help you.

7. Use a red colored pencil to **draw** the path of the Grand Tour leading from London to Rome. Show both the overland route and the water route.

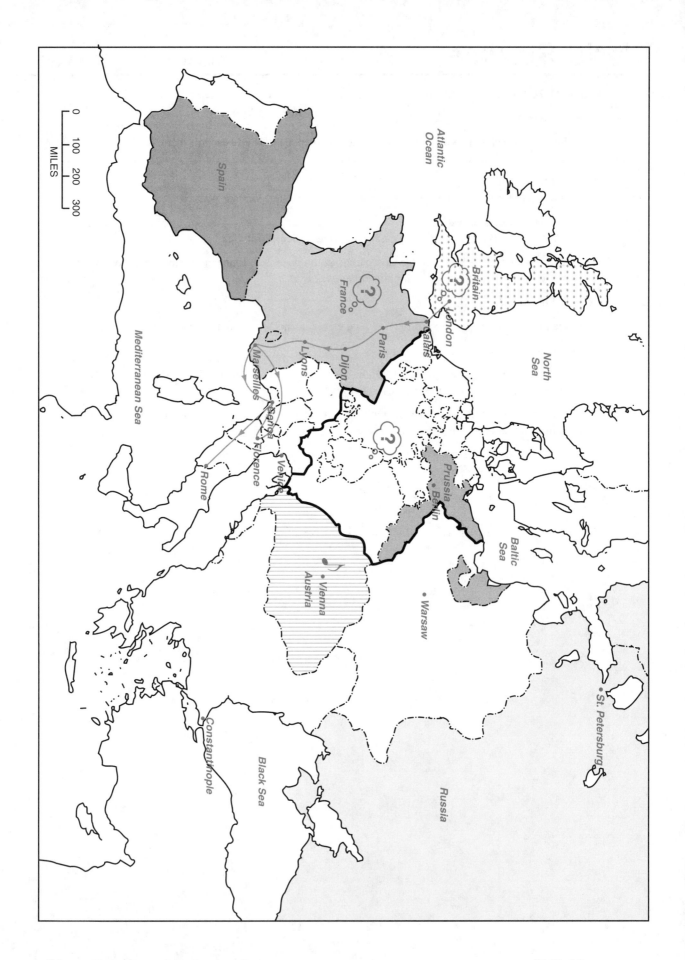

World Studies

Work Conditions

Factory work conditions during the Industrial Revolution were harsh for all ages. The following interview was evidence in a 1832 parliamentary investigation in England. The young woman being interviewed, Elizabeth Bentley, worked at a factory in Leeds. Read the passage and answer the questions at the end.

What age are you?
Twenty-three.
What time did you begin to work at a factory?
When I was six years old.
What kind of mill is it?
Flax mill.
What was your business in that mill?
I was a little doffer (A worker employed in removing full bobbins or spindles).
What were your hours of labour in that mill?
From 5 in the morning till 9 at night, when they were thronged (busy).
For how long a time together have you worked that excessive length of time?
For about half a year.
What were your usual hours when you were not so thronged?
From 6 in the morning till 7 at night.
What time was allowed for your meals?
Forty minutes at noon.
Had you any time to get your breakfast or drinking?
No, we got it as we could.
And when your work was bad, you had hardly any time to eat it at all?
No; we were obliged to leave it or take it home, and when we did not take it, the overlooker took it, and gave it to his pigs.
Explain what it is you had to do?
When the frames are full, they have to stop the frames, and take the flyers off, and take the full bobbins off, and carry them to the roller; and then put empty ones on, and set the frame going again.
Does that keep you constantly on your feet?
Yes, there are so many frames, and they run so quick.
Suppose you flagged (slowed down) a little or were too late. What would they do?
Strap us.
Are they in the habit of strapping those who are last in doffing?
Yes.
Constantly?
Yes.
Girls as well as boys?
Yes.
Have you ever been strapped?
Yes.
Severely?
Yes.
Could you eat your food well in that factory?
No, indeed I had not much to eat, and the little I had I could not eat it, my appetite was so poor, and being covered with dust; and it was no use to take it home, I could not eat it, and the overlooker took it and gave it to the pigs.
You are speaking of the breakfast?
Yes.

How far had you to go for dinner?

We could not go for dinner.

Where did you dine?

In the mill.

Supposing you had not been in time enough in the morning at these mills, what would have been the consequence?

We should have been quartered.

What do you mean by that?

If we were a quarter of an hour late, they would take off half of an hour; we only got a penny an hour, and they would take a halfpenny more.

Were you also beaten for being too late?

No, I was never beaten myself. I have seen boys beaten for being too late.

Were you generally there in time?

Yes; my mother had been up at 4 o'clock in the morning, and at 2 o'clock in the morning; the colliers (coal miners) used to go to their work about 3 or 4 o'clock, and when she heard them stirring she got up out of her warm bed and went and asked them the time; and I have sometimes been at Hunslet Car at 2 o'clock in the morning, when it was streaming down with rain, and we had to stay until the mill was opened.

Discussion Questions

1. How old was Elizabeth when she began working in the factory? How does this compare to the United States today? _Six; Today children rarely enter the work force so early. Instead they are allowed free public education._

2. At what type of factory did she work? _a flax mill_

3. Was this a textile factory? _yes_

4. What do you think was the source of power for the machines in the factory? _Answers may vary. Most factories were run by steam engines._

5. What was the usual punishment for slowing down or being late? _a strapping or receiving a pay cut (quartered)_

6. Were any of the workers beaten? _Yes, some of the boys were beaten for being late._

7. What was the earliest Elizabeth had arrived at the mill in the morning? _2 o'clock_

8. Why do you think Elizabeth's mother allowed her to work at the factory? _Answers will vary. Most often, children were made to work in order for the family to survive._

9. According to the textbook, what time of the day would John Wesley preach to factory workers like Elizabeth? _in the morning before their work began_

10. Despite the terrible conditions, what were the benefits of factory labor? _Many of the workers were poor. Without jobs like these, they and their families would have starved to death._

[More information on this subject can be found at http://landow.stg.brown.edu/victorian/history/workers1.html]

World Studies

Chapter 10   **Activity A**

Trivia Down Under

Play this game by writing the answers to each of the statements. If you are playing with a classmate, take turns writing in answers. When you are finished, use the text page numbers to check your answers. Total up the point values for your correct answers and write your final score in the box below.

	James Cook	First Fleet	Geography	Settling Austalia	Becoming a Nation
100	Name the bay where Captain Cook landed. p. 270 *Botany Bay*	The day the fleet arrived at Sydney Cove is now celebrated as this holiday. p. 272 *Australia Day*	These mountains are similar to the Appalachian Mountains in the United States. p. 268 *Great Dividing Range*	Along with two companions, he set out from his farm to cross the Blue Mountains. p. 274 *Gregory Blaxland*	In 1927 this city became the capital of Australia. p. 278 *Canberra*
200	Captain Cook used this to fight scurvy. p. 267 *sauerkraut*	The fleet's captain found this port and decided to settle there. p. 272 *Port Jackson*	This 1,250-mile series of coral reefs is off Australia's coast. p. 268 *Great Barrier Reef*	Explorers founded this colony around Perth in 1836. p. 275 *South Australia*	In 1856 all the colonies were granted self-government except this one. p. 278 *Western Australia*
300	This is the name Cook gave to the land he claimed in Australia. p. 271 *New South Wales*	This is the name of the First Fleet's captain. p. 272 *Arthur Phillips*	These people became hostile only when their land was settled by the English. p. 271 *Aborigines*	Sheep farmers found this land, which became an Australian colony in 1854. p. 275 *Victoria*	In 1901 Australia became a nation under this name. p. 278 *Commonwealth of Australia*
400	This was the name of Captain Cook's lead ship. p. 271 *Endeavour*	Convicts were sent to Australia when use of this American colony was cut off. p. 271 *Georgia*	This island of Australia was discovered by a Dutch explorer. p. 262 *Tasmania*	This land was so full of squatters that the government made it a colony. p. 275 *Queensland*	Australia's early industries were this type. p. 278 *import-substitution industries*
500	Cook was the first person to sail completely around this continent. p. 266 *Antarctica*	This was why the first supply ship never reached the colonists. p. 273 *It struck an iceberg and sank.*	This is the name for the area west of Australia's mountains. p. 268 *Outback*	John Ruse settled next to this river in Australia. p. 274 *Parramatta River*	This was the reason many settlers came to Australia in the 1850s. p. 278 *a gold rush*

Score 1:	Score 2:

World Studies

Pacific Islands

Using outside sources and the map on page 280 of your text, place the following islands and groups of islands in the proper categories below.

Islands

American Samoa
Belau
Cook Islands
Easter Island
Fiji
Guam
Hawaiian Islands
Kiribati
Marquesas Islands
Marshall Islands
Micronesia
Midway Islands
Nauru
New Caledonia
New Zealand
Papua New Guinea
Pitcairn
Samoa
Society Islands
Solomon Islands
Tahiti
Tokelau Islands
Tonga
Funafuti (Tuvalu)
Vanuatu

Melanesia	Micronesia	Polynesia
Fiji	Belau	American Samoa
New Caledonia	Guam	Cook Islands
Papua New Guinea	Kiribati	Easter Island
Solomon Islands	Marshall Islands	Hawaiian Islands
Vanuatu	Micronesia	Marquesas Islands
	Nauru	Midway Islands
		New Zealand
		Pitcairn
		Samoa
		Society Islands
		Tahiti
		Tokelau Islands
		Tonga
		Funafuti (Tuvalu)

From the list given, find the islands or island groups owned by these countries.

Chile: _Easter Island_

France: _Marquesas Islands, New Caledonia, Society Islands, and Tahiti_

New Zealand: _Cook Islands and Tokelau Islands_

United States: _American Samoa, Guam, Hawaiian Islands, and Midway Islands_

Identify the following Pacific islands as high or low islands.

Island(s)

Bougainville (Solomon Islands)
Funafuti (Tuvalu)
Midway Islands
Nauru
Tahiti

High	Low
Bougainville	Funafuti
Tahiti	Midway Islands
	Nauru

World Studies

Map Study—Australia and New Zealand

Refer to text pages 268 and 275.

1. **Label** Australia and use a colored pencil to **shade** it yellow.

2. **Label** New Zealand and use a colored pencil to **shade** it blue.

3. **Label** these physical features:
   Bodies of Water—Coral Sea, Great Australian Bight, Gulf of Carpentaria, Indian Ocean, Tasman Sea, Timor Sea, Torres Strait
   Mountains—Great Dividing Range, Southern Alps
   Regions—Arnhem Land, Outback
   Miscellaneous—Great Barrier Reef

4. **Label** these states and territories in Australia:
   New South Wales, Northern Territory, Queensland, South Australia, Tasmania, Victoria, Western Australia

5. **Label** the two main islands that form New Zealand.

6. **Write** in each state the year it became part of Australia.

7. **Draw** the Dutch icon in the part of Australia that Abel Tasman discovered.

   (**D**) Dutch

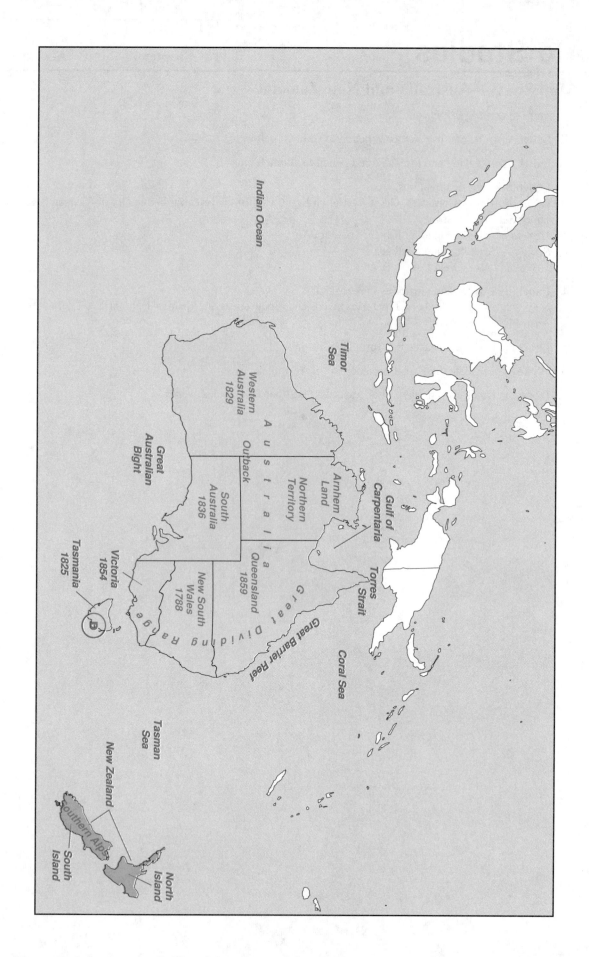

Reinforcement: Section 2-3

World Studies

Pacific Explorers

Based on the information in your text, answer the questions on each of these explorers.

Alvaro de Mendaña

1. For what country did he explore?   *Spain* _____

2. What was the purpose of his explorations?   *to find the rich lands to the west that the Spanish had* _____
   heard about from the Incas _____

3. What Pacific lands did he visit or discover?   *the Solomon Islands, the Marquesas, and Santa Cruz* ___
   _____

4. Why was Mendaña's crew discontent with him on the first expedition?   *They believed his* _____
   appointment as captain was due to his position as the viceroy's nephew rather than his experience. ___
   _____

5. What types of experiences did Mendaña have with the natives?   *The Spanish and the natives did not* ___
   get along well. Mendaña's crew used force to get supplies on the Solomon Islands. Men were killed on both
   sides. More natives were killed on the Marquesas after the natives stole from the Spanish. ___
   _____

Abel Tasman

6. For what country did he explore?   *the Netherlands* _____

7. What was the purpose of his exploration?   *to search for the unknown southern land* _____

8. What Pacific lands did he visit or discover?   *Tasmania and New Zealand* _____

9. Why were Tasman's discoveries kept secret for a while?   *The Dutch East India Company wanted to* ___
   avoid drawing other countries' attention to the area. _____

10. What types of experiences did he have with the natives?   *On Tasmania the natives shied away from the*
    Dutch. However, on New Zealand, the native Maoris attacked Tasman's men, killing four. ___
    _____

Louis Antoine de Bougainville

11. For what country did he explore?   *France* _____

12. What was the purpose of his exploration?   *to search for Terra Australis Incognita* _____

13. What Pacific lands did he visit or discover?   *Tahiti and the Solomon Islands* _____

14. Who were the two scientists on the voyage and what kind of scientists were they?   *Philibert* _____
    Commerson and Antoine Véron; naturalist and astronomer _____

15. Why did Bougainville settle and eventually abandon the Falkland Islands?   *He settled the islands to* ___
    regain power and respect for France following her losses in the New World. The settlement was abandoned
    because of rival claims by the English and Spanish. _____

James Cook

16. For what country did he explore? *England*

17. What was the purpose of his exploration? *to discover the real truth about the "unknown southern land" and claim land for England*

18. What Pacific lands did he visit or discover? *Australia, New Zealand, and Hawaii*

19. What part does Cook play in the history of Australia? *Cook landed at Botany Bay in 1770, claimed the land for England as New South Wales, and surveyed the eastern coast of the continent.*

20. What types of experiences did he have with the natives? *Cook generally treated the natives fairly and generously. He was the first white man to make peaceful contact with the Maoris of New Zealand. However, on Hawaii the natives reacted violently when Cook tried to take a chief hostage for stealing. In the resulting fight, Cook was killed.*

World Studies

Chapter 10   **Activity E**

Geography Skills

Case # 2:

Travelers and airlines worldwide are in shock after learning that luggage has been disappearing mysteriously. The only clues to the disappearances have been notes that people with lost luggage have received in their mail. The notes contain clips from travel brochures giving clues to the luggage locations. The GIA has analyzed the handwriting and matched it with the notorious prankster Sally Chiff. Once again the GIA and the world have called upon Sir Vey to solve the case. His job is to figure out the clues, find the lost luggage, and apprehend Miss Chiff. Use the maps on pages 610-14 of the text to help Sir Vey unravel the clues.

1. **"Enjoy an exciting voyage across this vast ocean that separates Europe from North and South America."**

   Which ocean should Sir Vey be looking in?   _Atlantic Ocean_

2. **"Along the coast of Brazil, you'll enter the mouth of the great river. Traveling westward just below the equator, you'll finally reach those wonderful mountains that extend down the western side of the continent."**

   At what river and mountain range should Sir Vey search for the luggage?   _Amazon River; Andes_

   Mountains

3. **"As you pass through the Alps, you'll finally arrive at its highest peak and discover just how thin the air is up there!"**

   On what peak should Sir Vey look for the luggage?   _Mt. Blanc_

4. **"From these mountains you can head east to visit the Caspian Sea or head west to visit the Black Sea."**

   Which mountain range should Sir Vey visit?   _Caucasus Mountains_

5. **"Come enjoy an intense journey among these mountains. If you're not frozen solid, you may even get to see the source of the Ganges and Indus Rivers!"**

   Which mountain range should Sir Vey explore?   _Himalayas_

6. **"From the frigid waters of Hudson Bay, you'll head south to the biggest and closest of the Great Lakes."**

   In which Great Lake is the luggage hidden?   _Lake Superior_

7. **"Our cruise ship will set sail from Italy and spend three days and three nights on that beautiful sea that reaches all the way to the northern coast of Africa."**

   In what sea is the luggage hidden?   _Mediterranean Sea_

8. **"Traveling by foot, you'll follow the longest river in the world until you come to that famous lake on the equator."**

   At what river and lake should Sir Vey look for the luggage?   _Nile River; Lake Victoria_

9. **"From this country you can visit the Arabian Sea and the Bay of Bengal while remaining comfortably at a latitude of 20 degrees north of the equator!"**

   In what country will Sir Vey find the luggage?   _India_

10. **"After crossing the Great Sandy Desert, you'll travel to these mountains on the eastern side of the continent."**

Which continent and mountain range should Sir Vey visit?   *Australia; Great Dividing Range*

11. **"Enjoy the scenery as you travel across this desert south of Lake Baykal and north of the Yellow River."**

In which desert is the luggage hidden?   *Gobi Desert*

12. **"As you cross this desert, you'll be thinking about all that water in the Mediterranean Sea to the north, the Atlantic Ocean to the west and south, and the Nile River to the east. You'll wear with pride your complimentary 'I crossed the largest desert in the world' T-shirt—if you survive."**

In what desert is the luggage hidden?   *Sahara*

13. **"Traveling south of the Congo River, you'll be able to visit your choice of deserts on the same continent—both conveniently located on the tropic of Capricorn!"**

In which two deserts should Sir Vey search?   *Namib Desert and Kalahari Desert*

14. **"After a fun trip to the Atacama Desert, you'll travel north to the Andes to visit the highest navigable lake in the world."**

Which continent should Sir Vey visit? What is the name of the lake where the luggage is located?

South America; Lake Titicaca

15. **"Set sail with us as we head from the mouth of the Mississippi River to the coast of South America."**

In which gulf and sea should Sir Vey search?   *Gulf of Mexico; Caribbean Sea*

16. **"Imagine the fun you'll have as you head from Asia into Europe crossing these mountains. They stretch along a longitude of 60 degrees east of the prime meridian and extend as far north as the Arctic Circle."**

Which mountains should Sir Vey visit?   *Ural Mountains*

17. **"Experience the thrill of adventure and the crashing of waves as your ship sails from the Baltic Sea into this one!"**

In what sea is the luggage hidden?   *North Sea*

18. **"You'll spend more time than you ever wanted to visiting the only ocean that touches North America, Europe, and Asia."**

In which ocean is the luggage hidden?   *Arctic Ocean*

19. **"Enjoy Europe at high altitude as you cross the only mountain range that extends from the coastline on the Atlantic Ocean to that on the Mediterranean Sea!"**

In which mountain range should Sir Vey search?   *Pyrenees*

20. **"Following a scenic voyage on the Indian Ocean, you'll sail along the coast of Africa to this sea on the tropic of Cancer!"**

In what sea is the luggage hidden?   *Red Sea*

21. **"Although they're not as high as the Rocky Mountains, you'll enjoy your visit to these mountains found on the eastern side of the same continent."**

In which mountains range should Sir Vey search?   *Appalachian Mountains*

World Studies

Communications

Using additional resources, find the following information for these inventions. Think of three more communications inventions, research them, and place the information in the last three rows.

In some cases more than one inventor may be named.

Invention	Inventor(s)	Year of Inventions	Purpose
Telephone	Alexander Graham Bell	1876	*to send and receive auditory messages over long distances*
Typewriter	*Christopher Sholes*	*1860*	*to produce printed letters and figures on paper*
Camera	*George Eastman*	*1888*	*to capture images on film*
Telegraph	*William F. Cooke* *Charles Wheatstone*	*1837*	*to send and receive encoded messages over long distances*
Television	*John Logie Baird* *Vladimir K. Zworykin*	*1925* *1929*	*to transit moving pictures and sounds*
Radio	*R. A. Fessenden* *Guglielmo Marconi*	*1900* *1901*	*to send auditory messages to a mass audience*
Video tape recorder	*A. Poniatoff*	*1956*	*to record visual images onto tape*

Inventions in communications have affected many different fields. Examine one invention in each field and consider its impact.

Business

Invention: _____

Impact of field: *Answers will vary.* _____

_____

Arts

Invention: _____

Impact on field: *Answers will vary.* _____

_____

Education

Invention: _____

Impact on field: *Answers will vary.* _____

_____

Politics

Invention: _____

Impact on field: *Answers will vary.* _____

_____

World Studies

Mystery Word

Read each statement carefully. Write the answers in the blanks and then unscramble the numbered letters to find the mystery word.

1. Freedom, nationalism, and nature are a few of the characteristics of this style of art.

   R O M A N T I C I S M
           1

2. He was the leading opera composer of the time.

   G U I S E P P E   V E R D I
       2

3. This theory states that all living creatures came from nonliving elements.

   E V O L U T I O N
                   3

4. This style of art emphasized reality.

   R E A L I S M
       4

5. Some argue that he is the only truly impressionistic composer.

   C L A U D E   D E B U S S Y
       5

6. This belief taught that people could be improved through changes in their living conditions.

   S O C I A L   G O S P E L
               6

7. This organization was intended to meet people's spiritual and physical needs.

   S A L V A T I O N   A R M Y
       7

8. His mix of classical and romantic music made him probably the best-known composer of this age.

   L U D W I G   V A N   B E E T H O V E N
                               8

9. He believed that man had formed over millions of years of adaptation.

   C H A R L E S   D A R W I N
           9

10. His preaching helped to bring many to the Lord during the 1800s.

    C H A R L E S   H.   S P U R G E O N
                                   10

11. This romantic composer used folksongs in his works.

    F R É D É R I C   C H O P I N
                           11

12. He used realistic elements in his stories of working-class Englishmen.

    C H A R L E S   D I C K E N S
           12

Mystery Word

The nineteenth century is often called

the V I C T O R I A N   A G E .

World Studies

Map Study—England

Refer to text page 298.

1. **Label** England and use a colored pencil to shade it yellow.

2. **Label** these features of physical geography:
   Bodies of Water—Atlantic Ocean, English Channel, Irish Sea, North Sea, Strait of Dover
   Mountains—Pennines, Scafell Pike
   Regions—Lake District

3. **Label** the following countries:
   Belgium, Denmark, Ireland, Germany, Netherlands, Norway

4. **Label** these political units within the United Kingdom:
   Northern Ireland, Scotland, Wales

5. **Locate** and **label** the city of London and then **place** the icon for the Crystal Palace next to it.

    Crystal Palace

Using Additional Resources—

Use an atlas, encyclopedia, or other resources to complete the following.

6. **Find** Manchester, England, and then **locate** it on your map to represent the approximate location of New Lanark mentioned on page 301 of your text. **Place** the factory town icon next to this site.

    factory town

7. **Find** Bristol, England, and then **locate** and **label** it on your map. **Place** the orphanage icon by it to represent George Mueller's orphanage there.

    orphanage

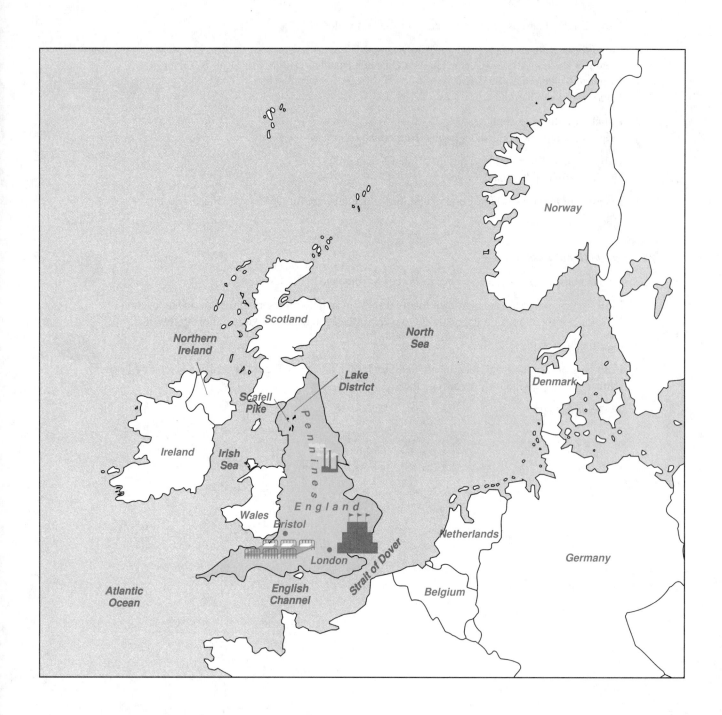

World Studies

Map Study—Europe in the 1800s

Refer to text pages 304 and 306.

1. Use a yellow colored pencil to **shade** the country that became independent from the Ottoman Empire in 1829. **Label** this country.

2. Use a blue colored pencil to **shade** the country that became independent from the Netherlands in 1831. **Label** this country.

3. Use a green colored pencil to **shade** those countries that were born in 1871. **Label** each of these countries.

4. **Label** the following countries:
   Austria, France, Netherlands, Poland, Switzerland

Using Additional Resources—

Use an atlas, encyclopedia, or other resources to complete the following.

5. **Find** the nationality of these people and **place** in those countries the icon best associated with that person:
   Karl Marx, Claude Debussy, Frédéric Chopin, Giuseppe Verdi, Prince Metternich

    ruler

   / writer

   ♪ composer

6. Napoleon was born on the island of Corsica. **Find** and **label** this island, and **place** the proper icon for Napoleon there.

    ruler

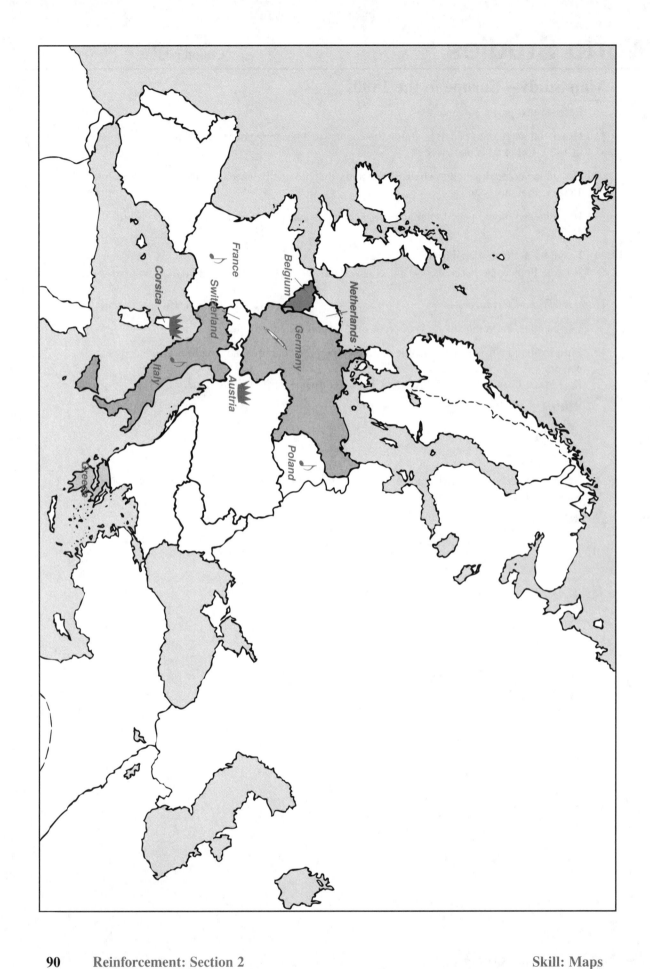

World Studies

Nationalism

As in the nineteenth century, nationalism is a strong force in the world today. Many current political conflicts are linked to nationalist movements. Complete the profiles on these current national conflicts in the world. You will need to consult outside sources such as newspapers, magazines, or encyclopedias.

The former Yugoslavia:

One of the most notable nationalistic conflicts has been that in the former Yugoslavia. The country was created during World War I from a movement for Southern Slavic unity. However, the union was unstable, and soon the many Slavic groups began arguing among themselves. Look at Yugoslavia on the map on page 431. Compare it with the map on page 437. Note how the country changed between World War II and the present.

Choose one of the following conflicts to research. Write a paragraph on your topic on the lines below. Try to include when the conflict began, what the major events have been, and who the important leaders are.

COUNTRY/GROUP SEEKING INDEPENDENCE
Israel/Palestine
Canada/Quebec
Turkey/Kurds
Russia/Chechnya
Spain/Basques
France/Britany

_____

_____

_____

_____

_____

_____

_____

_____

_____

_____

_____

_____

_____

_____

_____

_____

_____

World Studies

Political Cartoons

　　Not everyone agreed with Rudyard Kipling's views expressed in "The White Man's Burden." Some Americans believed that U.S. involvement in the Philippines was the beginning of American imperialism. Analyze the following political cartoons. Tell who is represented, what the cartoonist is trying to say, and how these cartoons contrast with Kipling's views. *Some people considered the United States an imperial power because of its involvement and control over the Philippines.*

*　　The riders in the cartoon represent those nations involved in imperialism—specifically the United States, Great Britain, Germany, and France. The ones carrying them are natives of those countries where imperialistic powers were moving in. The cartoonist is saying that the burden in imperialism is not on the white man but on the natives of the countries. In contrast, Kipling saw imperialism as a way of helping the natives of these countries.*

_____

_____

_____

_____

THE WHITE (?) MAN'S BURDEN.

THE WHITE MAN'S BURDEN.—*The Ram's Horn, Chicago.*

*　　In this cartoon the two figures represent militarism and industry. The cartoonist believed the imperialistic goal of building industry was being used to support the military class. Using natives in industry freed up more people for the military in these imperialistic nations. While Kipling saw imperialism as a way of helping the native peoples of the world, this cartoonist saw it as a military tool and a burden on these peoples.*

_____

_____

_____

_____

World Studies

Chapter 12   **Activity B**

Before and After

List the conditions that existed in India before and after the British came.

	Before British Rule	**After British Rule**
Agriculture	• *primitive farming* • *famine a constant threat*	• *better equipment, methods, management, and research* • *irrigation canals built* • *emergency relief plan* • *tea and rubber industries*
Industry	• *raw materials available* • *manufactured goods imported*	• *mills, factories, iron- and steel-works built in some cities*
Transportation/ Communication	• *travel mostly by foot or oxcart* • *slow communications*	• *railroad systems developed* • *telegraph and postal system improve communications*
Education	• *few receive formal education*	• *government and missionary schools opened* • *education in English instead of Sanskrit*
Social Practices	• *little regard for personal freedom* • *suttee is practiced* • *women are forbidden to remarry*	• *suttee is made illegal* • *women are allowed to remarry*

Discussion Questions

1. Why were the British able to make so many changes in India despite their small numbers in comparison to the people of India?   *Answers will vary. Although there were fewer British than Indians, the British had several advantages. They had military force and technology. They also had wealth coming from the rest of the Empire to invest in changing India.*

2. Do you think that overall the British had a positive or negative influence on India?

   Answers will vary. The British did destroy some of the native culture they found, but some of the Indian practices (such as suttee) were terrible. More importantly, British involvement in India opened a door for missions. Carey and Ward spread the truth of the gospel throughout the land.

World Studies

Map Study—South Asia

Refer to text page 328.

1. **Label** India and use a colored pencil to **shade** it green.

2. **Label** these features of physical geography:
   Bodies of Water—Arabian Sea, Bay of Bengal, Indian Ocean
   Rivers—Brahmaputra River, Ganges River, Indus River
   Mountains—Eastern Ghats, Himalayas, Western Ghats
   Miscellaneous—Deccan Plateau, Thar Desert

3. **Label** the following countries:
   Afghanistan, Bangladesh, Bhutan, China, Nepal, Pakistan, Sri Lanka, Tajikistan, Turkmenistan

4. Using the information on page 324 and the map on page 326:
   Locate and **label** the first three trading centers the East India Company had in South Asia.

Using Additional Resources—

Use an atlas, encyclopedia, or other resources to complete the following.

5. **Find** Meerut, India, where violence erupted during the Sepoy Mutiny. **Place** the battle icon there on the map to show its location.
    battle

6. **Place** the battle icon between Calcutta and the Ganges River directly to the north. The Battle of Plassey took place around here. Next to the site, **place** the nation icons of the two European countries that were involved in the fighting.
    battle
   (F) France
   (GB) Great Britain

World Studies

Cryptograms

Use the clues to decode the words below. Then use the code to read the quotation on the next page.

1. He was the hero of the Battle of Plassey.

   Robert Clive

   FBMSFW OEQTS

2. This word means "master" in Hindu.

   sahib

   LGKQM

3. She was the first woman missionary to India.

   Hannah Marshman

   KGIIGK PGFLKPGI

4. He was a printer who worked with Carey.

   William Ward

   HQEEQGP HGFC

5. These were Indians who studied in British universities.

   babus

   MGMJL

6. This is the name for the official British rule in India.

   British Raj

   MFQWQLK FGZ

7. These winds bring much rain through India.

   monsoons

   PBILBBIL

8. This company had centers at Bombay, Madras, and Calcutta.

   East India Company

   SGLW QICQG OBPVGIU

9. This is an ancient Indian language.

   Sanskrit

   LGILNFQW

10. This act required troops to serve anywhere the British deemed necessary.

    General Enlistment Act

    ASISFGE SIEQLWPSIW GOW

Perhaps this quotation from Rudyard Kipling's *Just So Stories* explains how he was able to write about so many different subjects.

I keep six honest serving men

Q NSSV LQC KBISLW LSFTQIA PSI

(They taught me all I knew);

WKSU WGJAKW PS GEE Q NISH

Their names are What and Why and When

WKSQF IGPSL GFS HKGW GIC HKU GIC HKSI

And How and Where and Who.

GIC KBH GIC HKSFS GIC HKB

World Studies

Chapter 13   **Activity A**

Missionary Information

Chapters 12 and 13 have highlighted some of the major figures in Far East missions. Today, others are continuing the Lord's work in this area. Write to a missionary or missionary family in the Far East and find out as much information as you can about them. Record the information under the headings below. Report your findings to the class in a two- to three-minute presentation.

Names of missionaries: _____

Children (ages): _____   _____

_____   _____

_____   _____

Mission board: _____

Country of service: _____   Type of government: _____

Physical description of their city/town/village:

_____

_____

_____

Area's major religion(s):   General attitude of people toward the gospel:

_____   _____

_____   _____

_____   _____

Greatest difficulties the missionaries face:

_____

_____

Brief testimonies by one or two of the family members:

_____

_____

_____

_____

Major prayer requests:

_____

_____

_____

Other interesting information:

_____

_____

_____

Mission card: (attach to page with staple or paper clip)

World Studies

News Briefs

In each box write a brief news article based on the time and place given. Remember to answer the journalistic questions of *who, what, where, when,* and *why*. Write as if you were a reporter in that place as the events were occurring. There may be some things you cannot include because they would not have taken place yet.

The specific date for article four is not given in the text. Some teacher explanation may be needed.

March 10, 1839—Canton, China: *High Commissioner Lin Tse-hsü gave a sharp warning to British traders today. After arriving in Canton, Tse-hsü confronted the traders about the importing of opium into China. He demanded that the British hand over their unsold opium to the Chinese government and that they stop importing the substance. Tse-hsü gave the British two weeks to comply with his demands.*

July 8, 1853—Japan: *Several American warships were spotted off the coast today near the city of Yedo. The commander of the fleet, Commodore Matthew Perry, has met with the shogun to discuss trade relations between the two countries. Apparently, the Americans want Japan to open its doors to trade with the United States. Perry has given Japan one year to respond to the American request. Opinions in Japan are mixed. Some favor trade with the United States, while others want to preserve Japan's isolation.*

June 20, 1900—Peking, China: *Boxer forces attacked the Legation Quarter of Peking today. Citizens of other nations have become the target of the Boxers, a society whose goal is to exterminate foreigners. In response, foreign nations have sent troops to the Imperial City to fight the Boxers. It may be several days before they are able to break the siege. Many of the Chinese resent the spheres of influence that nations like Britain, France, and Portugal have been trying to create within the country.*

July 1, 1997—Hong Kong: *Great Britain returned control of Hong Kong to the Chinese government today. Since 1860, the British have controlled the Kowloon Peninsula where Hong Kong is located. In 1898 they signed an agreement with China to lease the port for ninety-nine years. The lease ended today. Although Hong Kong is once again part of China, it remains somewhat independent. As part of the Sino-British Joint Declaration in 1984, it was agreed that the port would retain control of its government and economy for fifty years. In recent years, the British have been preparing Hong Kong for self-rule. Just how much independence Hong Kong will have is a question only China can answer. The wealthy port will be watched closely in the next few years.*

World Studies

Map Study—Southeast Asia

Refer to text page 360.

1. **Label** these features of physical geography:
   Bodies of Water—Bay of Bengal, Gulf of Thailand, Indian Ocean, Pacific Ocean, South China Sea
   Mountains—Bilauktaung Range
   Islands—Irian Jaya, Java, Kalimantan, Sulawesi, Sumatra

2. **Label** the following countries:
   Brunei, Cambodia, Indonesia, Laos, Malaysia, Myanmar, Philippines, Singapore, Thailand, Vietnam

3. **Place** the Manchu icon within or next to these countries that were once tributary states of the empire: [former name(s)in parentheses]
   Cambodia, Laos, Myanmar (Burma), Thailand (Siam), Vietnam (Annam, Cochin China, Tonkin)
    Manchu

4. **Place** the Britain icon within or next to the following countries that were once British territories:
   Brunei, Malaysia, Singapore
    Great Britain

5. **Place** the United States icon within the Philippines to show U.S. annexation of the islands in 1898.
    United States

Using Additional Resources—

Use an atlas, encyclopedia, or other resources to complete the following.

6. One of the Chinese ports that opened between 1855 and 1890 was Chiung-chou on Hai-nan island. **Find** this island and **place** the port icon within it.
    port

7. Use a blue colored pencil to **draw** the routes of the Mekong and Irrawaddy Rivers in Southeast Asia.

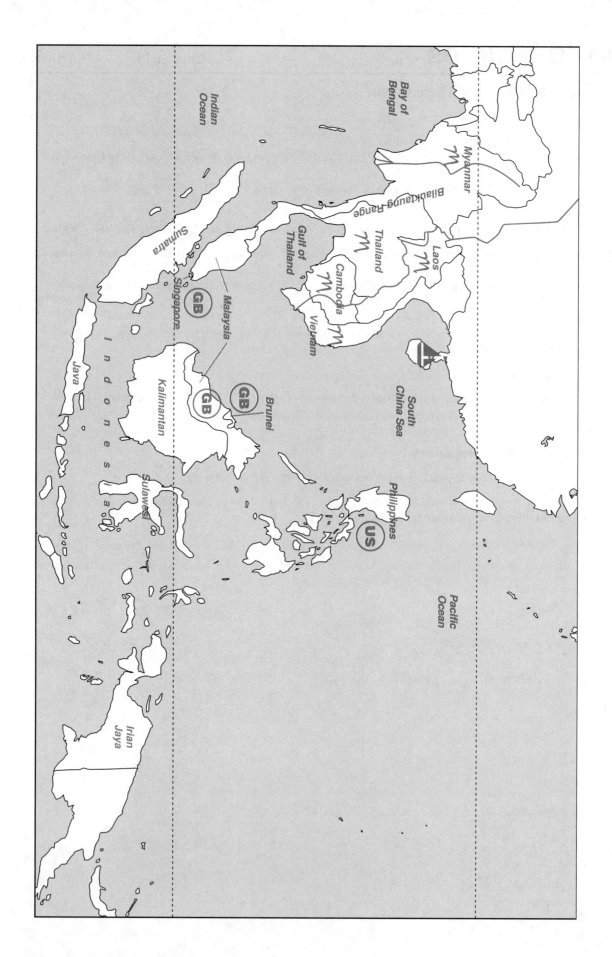

World Studies

Map Study—China and Japan

Refer to text pages 352 and 369.

1. **Draw** the borders of Manchuria in yellow and **label** the area.

2. **Locate** and **label** the following ports and then **place** the appropriate nation icons next to them:
   Hong Kong, Kwangchou, Macao, Port Arthur, Tsingtao, Weihaiwei

   (GB) Great Britain

   (F) France

   (P) Portugal

   (R) Russia

   (G) Germany

3. Both Formosa and Korea were once territories of Japan. **Label** each and **place** the Japan icon next to them.

   (J) Japan

Using Additional Resources—

Use an atlas, encyclopedia, or other resources to complete the following.

4. **Label** the Huang He (Yellow River) and the Chang River (Yangtze).

5. **Find** the following Japanese and Korean ports and **place** the port icon at these locations:
   Inchon, Nagasaki, Niigata, Osaka, Pusan, Wonsan, Yokohama

    port

6. **Find** the cities of Nanjing (Nanking) and Beijing (Peking) and then **locate** and **label** them on the map. **Place** the battle icon by both. Nanjing was seiged during the Taiping Rebellion, and Beijing was a center of fighting during the Boxer Rebellion.

   ✗✗ battle

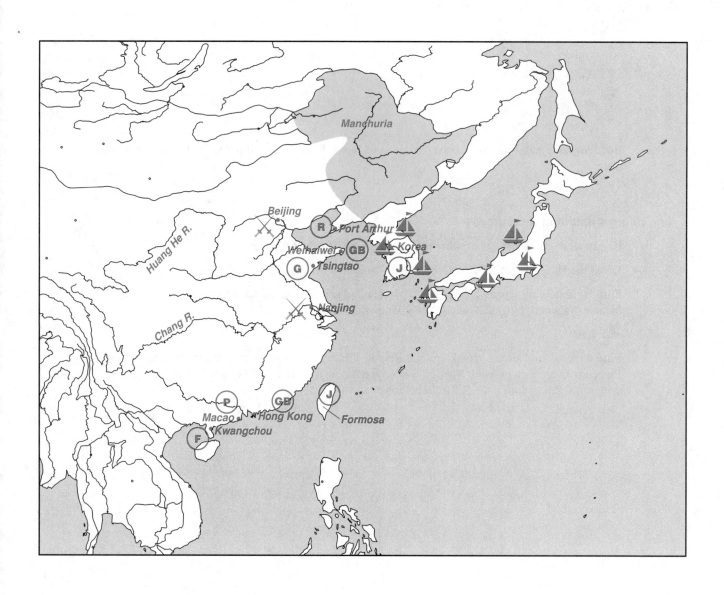

World Studies

Read and Underline

As you read the following passage, examine the words in bold type. Underline the choice that correctly completes each sentence.

The traditional Chinese name for their land was *Chung Kuo*, or **the Central Kingdom/Manchuria**. For a time the Chinese were ruled by the Mongols, but eventually they overthrew them and established the **Manchu/Ming** dynasty. During this time craftsmen perfected **iron/porcelain** production and exported these products.

Throughout history China has seen itself as superior to other countries. A British trade agreement with China failed after ambassador Lord Macartney failed to **pay tribute/perform the kowtow.** For most of the eighteenth century, foreign trade in China was limited to **Canton/the Imperial City.** Eventually **American/English** merchants began to make a profit by importing large amounts of opium into China. China's High Commissioner **Ch'i-shan/Lin Tse-hsü** destroyed a large quantity of opium turned over by the British government. The tense situation resulted in the Opium War. The war ended with the signing of the **Sino-British Joint Declaration/Treaty of Nanking.**

During the nineteenth century, foreign missionaries began to come to China. One of the earliest missionaries, **William Carey/Robert Morrison,** came to China in 1807. He was followed by Hudson Taylor, who established the China Inland Mission. During the wars and rebellions of the century, some missionaries lost their lives. Jonathan Goforth and his wife made a narrow escape during the **Boxer Rebellion/Taiping Rebellion.**

The Taiping Rebellion was initiated by a **government official/student** named Hung Hsiu-chuan. Hung had visions where he saw himself in the **"Ring of Fire"/"Thirty-third Heaven."** Eventually the rebellion died with Hung's suicide and the defeat of his men. One British soldier, named Charles Gordon, became famous for his leadership of the **rebel/imperial** forces during the conflict.

In 1894 war broke out between China and Japan. The two countries fought for control of **Korea/the Malay Archipelago.** The result was a resounding defeat for **China/Japan**. Many European countries were interested in claiming land in China. They sought to do this by establishing **Legation Quarters/spheres of influence** within China.

The Boxer Rebellion began in **1899/1902.** Although the Boxers first opposed the Chinese government, an alliance was eventually formed between the two. The secret society's slogan was "Support the Qing and **conquer Japan."/exterminate foreigners."** European forces defeated the Boxers and established a new government in China. This new government was unstable and was eventually replaced by a **Communist/democratic** one.

World Studies

Exploring Africa

Make a spinner like the one shown and use a small object to represent Sir Vey. Try to navigate him all the way down the Nile to the source of the river. For review afterward, go over the questions you skipped.

On a separate sheet of paper, copy or trace the circle, arrow, and game piece below. Do NOT cut out the examples. When you have the pieces copied, cut them out. Using the end of your pencil, punch a small hole in the center of the circle. Tape the arrow to a flat surface. Place the circle slightly under the arrow as shown in the diagram. Place the tip of your pencil in the punched hole and spin the spinner. Use the game piece to mark your place as you proceed around the board.

If you plan to use the game as a class activity, copy one spinner for each group of four or five students. Use heavyweight paper such as poster board or manila folders. Copy enough game pieces for your entire class. Give these pieces to the students prior to playing the game so that they can color them for easy identification.

1   2

EXAMPLE

4   3

Do NOT cut out the example.

This river is now considered to be the farthest source of the Nile.
Ruvironza River

David Livingstone discovered this waterfall.
Victoria Falls

He was the one who finally found Dr. Livingstone in Africa.
Henry Stanley

Burton and Speke believed this lake was the source of the Nile River.
Lake Victoria

The capital of Liberia was named for him.
James Monroe

This is the name for the rush by European nations to get African territory.
the Scramble

The desert is located in the interior of Southern Africa.
Kalahari Desert

Explorers in **western** Africa charted the course of this river.
Niger River

King Leopold used this organization to carve out a slice of Africa.
International African Association

Britain took control of Egypt in order to protect this canal.
the Suez Canal

Henry Stanley found David Livingstone on the shores of this lake.
Lake Tanganyika

He built the Suez Canal.
Ferdinand de Lesseps

This is the name for Dutch settlers in Africa.
Boers

She was killed while on an expedition across the Sahara.
Alexandrine Tinné

He was the German chancellor at the time of the partitioning of Africa.
Otto von Bismarck

The process of dividing up an area on paper is known as this.
partitioning

This land was set up as a home for former slaves.
Liberia

The Great Trek occurred after the British took over this colony.
Cape Colony

After returning to England, he took full credit for discovering the source of the Nile.
John Speke

This Scotsman was the most famous missionary to Africa in the nineteenth century.
David Livingstone

This act set the ground rules for claiming territory in Africa.
Berlin Act

Leopold's slice of Africa was located along this river.
Congo River

One Greek explorer claimed the "Mountains of the Moon" were the source of this river.
Nile River

Although motivated by selfishness and greed, he was known as "the greatest humanitarian of his time."
King Leopold II

This was the name of the territory Leopold carved out of Africa.
Belgian Congo

Because of sickness he had to wait while his partner reached Lake Victoria.
Richard Burton

In 1909 the people of South Africa formed this.
Union of South Africa

This Scottish missionary served fifty-one years in South Africa.
Robert Moffat

This desert is located on the west coast of Southern Africa.
Namib Desert

The purpose of this meeting of European leaders was to set down rules for dividing Africa.
Berlin Conference

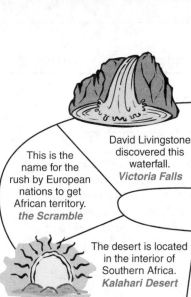

World Studies

Chapter 14   **Activity B**

Time Line

Using the information found in this chapter, fill in the events that go with the dates on the time line. In addition make personal time lines for David Livingstone, Robert Moffat, and Sir Richard Burton.

		Events	Tinné	Livingstone	Moffat	Burton
1790s					b. 1795	
	1798	Napoleon leads expedition in Egypt				
1800s	1807	*Parliament outlaws slave trade*				
1810s				b. 1813	1816 Contact with Methodists 1817 Arrives in Africa 1819 Marries Mary Smith	
	1821	*Liberia is founded*				b. 1821
1820s						
1830s	1833	*Slavery is outlawed in the British empire*				
	1836	*The Great Trek begins*				
1840s			b. 1839	1840 Arrives in Africa		
	1847	*Monrovia becomes capital of Liberia*				
1850s	1854	*Lesseps submits plans for Suez Canal*				1855 First Nile expedition 1858 Second Nile expedition
	1859	Work begins on the Suez Canal				
1860s			1863 Travels down the Nile			
			d. 1869			
1870s				d. 1873	1870 Ends work in South Africa	
	1876	*Leopold hosts convention*				
1880s	1880 1880 1882	*Laveran discovers cause of malaria* *Slave trade officially ended in world* *Leopold owns company resulting from IAA*				
	1884	*Berlin Act*				d. 1890
1890s	1897 1899	*Ross finds parasite in mosquitoes* Boer War begins				
1900s	1902	*Boer War ends*				
	1909	*Union of South Africa formed*				

World Studies

Chapter 14   **Activity C**

Map Study—Southern Africa

Refer to text page 390.

1. Use a red colored pencil to **trace** the border between Southern Africa and the rest of the continent.

2. **Label** these features of physical geography:
   Bodies of Water—Atlantic Ocean, Indian Ocean
   Deserts—Kalihari Desert, Namib Desert

3. **Label** the following countries:
   Angola, Botswana, Lesotho, Malawi, Mozambique, Namibia, South Africa, Swaziland, Zambia, Zimbabwe

4. **Find** the nationality of the Boers. **Place** their nation's icon and the British icon inside South Africa to represent the Boer War.
   (**D**) Netherlands
   (**GB**) Great Britain

5. The city of Mafeking is south of Gaborone, Botswana, just inside South Africa. **Place** the battle icon here to mark the site.
   ⚔ battle

Using Additional Resources—

Use an atlas, encyclopedia, or other resources to complete the following.

6. Use a blue colored pencil to **trace** and **label** the route of the Orange River in Southern Africa.

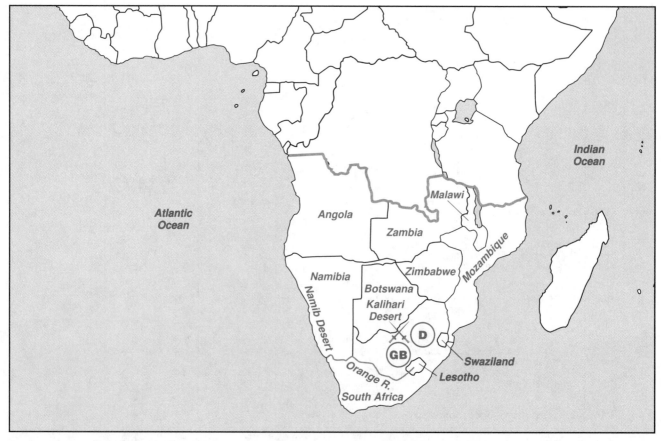

World Studies

Map Study—Physical Features of Africa

Refer to text page 388.

1. **Label** the following bodies of water:
   Lake Chad, Lake Nasser, Lake Nyasa, Lake Tanganyika, Lake Victoria

2. **Label** the following rivers:
   Blue Nile, Congo River, Niger River, White Nile, Zambezi River

3. **Label** Stanley Falls and Victoria Falls, and **place** the waterfall icon at each location.

   waterfall

4. **Circle** the location of the Suez Canal in Egypt. **Label** the canal region and **place** the appropriate nation icon to represent Ferdinand de Lesseps's nationality.

   (F) France

5. Using the map on page 110, **label** the Sahara. **Place** within the region the explorer icon and the correct nation's icon to represent Alexandrine Tinné.

   explorer

   (D) Netherlands

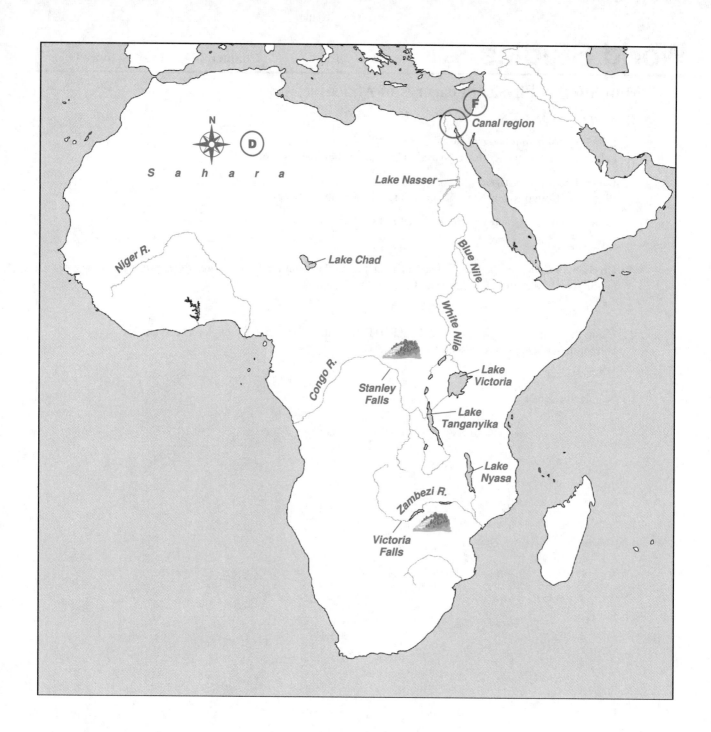

Sahara

N

D

Canal region

F

Lake Nasser

Niger R.

Lake Chad

Blue Nile

White Nile

Congo R.

Lake
Victoria

Stanley
Falls

Lake
Tanganyika

Lake
Nyasa

Zambezi R.

Victoria
Falls

World Studies

Map Study—Partitioning Africa

Refer to text page 399.

1. **Label** those parts of Africa claimed by the French, British, Germans, and Belgians. Use different colored pencils to **shade** each European country's territory and **create** a key to go with the map.

2. **Label** the country that became the home to many resettled slaves from the United States. **Place** the United States icon next to it.

   (US) United States

Using Additional Resources—

Use an atlas, encyclopedia, or other resources to complete the following.

3. The British were also involved in the Sudanese War of 1896-99. **Place** the battle icon inside Anglo-Egyptian Sudan to represent this conflict.

   ✗ battle

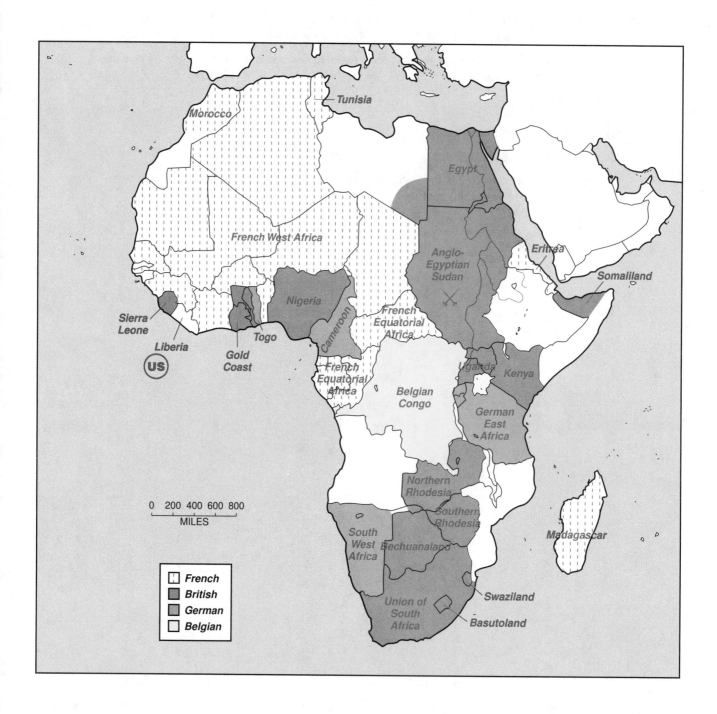

Sierra Leone

Liberia

US

Togo

Gold Coast

Morocco

Tunisia

French West Africa

Nigeria

Cameroon

French Equatorial Africa

French Equatorial Africa

Belgian Congo

Egypt

Anglo-Egyptian Sudan

Eritrea

Somaliland

Uganda

Kenya

German East Africa

Northern Rhodesia

Southern Rhodesia

South West Africa

Bechuanaland

Union of South Africa

Swaziland

Basutoland

Madagascar

0 200 400 600 800
MILES

French
British
German
Belgian

World Studies

David Livingstone's Letters

Read the following letter Livingstone wrote to family members back in Scotland. Answer the questions that follow.

September 30, 1853, to Mr. and Mrs. N. Livingstone and daughters

Through the mercy of God we reached this town after many and vexatious delays, and were received with many demonstrations of welcome. Every one seemed possessed with the idea that with a missionary some great indefinite good had arrived, but their ideas and mine are very different, though in one respect we agree. Many expected to be transformed at once into civilized men possessing the clothing goods, arms, horses, wagons, of the more favoured portions of humanity. They would not believe that all I could do would be to elevate them by plain open preaching and teaching. They expected a great deal from medicines used in the way of enchantments; and when I insisted that the only change I desired was a change of heart and conduct, they replied that Jesus had not loved their forefathers, hence their present degradation.

I was prevented by fever and other matters from at once following up the glorious object of this journey, viz. while preaching the gospel beyond every other man's line of things made ready to our hands, to discover a healthy location for a mission, and therefore determined to improve the time by teach-

ing to read. This produced profound deliberation and lengthy palavers, and at last the chief told me that he "feared learning to read would change his heart, and make him content with one wife, as in the case of Sechele." He has four.

I am trying now to establish the Lord's kingdom in a region wider by far than Scotland. Fever seems to forbid, but I shall work for the glory of Christ's Kingdom, fever or no fever. All the intelligent men who direct our Society and understand the nature of my movements support me warmly. A few I understand in Africa in writing home have styled my efforts as "wanderings." The very word contains a lie coiled like a serpent in its bosom. It means travelling without an object, or uselessly. . . . So very sure am I that I am in the path which Christ's kingdom is to be promoted, if the Society should object I would consider it my duty to withdraw from it. But at present, in accordance with the plan fully stated to the Society and public before setting out, I proceed to try & open up a short path to the West coast. We are immortal till our work is done. If I am cut off by fever, my efforts are no longer needed by Him who knows what is best.

1. How did the people from the town want Livingstone to change their lives? _*Answers may vary. They*_

   *wanted Livingstone to change them by giving them material goods.*

   _____

2. How did Livingstone want to change the people's lives? _*He wanted to change them inside by*_

   *preaching and teaching Christ.*

3. Why did the people believe they were in their present condition? _*They believed that Jesus Christ had*_

   *not loved their forefathers.*

4. How could this belief be disproved by using the Bible? (Give Scripture references.) _*Answers may*_

   *vary. Possible answers include Matthew 5:45, John 3:16, and John 9:1-3.*

   _____

5. What was the purpose of Livingstone's journey? _*His purpose was to preach the gospel, find a good*_

   *location for the mission, and teach the people to read.*

6. Why did the chief not want to learn to read? _*He was afraid that by learning to read he would*_

   *understand the Bible and it would make him change his lifestyle.*

7. How is his excuse similar to the excuses of other people who refuse to accept Christ? _Answers may vary. Some people refuse Christ because they know it will mean giving up their sinful ways._

8. Use a dictionary to look up the meaning of the word *palaver*. Write the meaning(s) on the following lines. _palaver: idle chatter; talk intended to charm or beguile; a parley between Eurpean explorers and representatives of local populations, especially in Africa_

9. What were some of the problems Livingstone faced in his work? _Livingstone faced physical problems through fevers. He also faced opposition from other missionaries who criticized his method of spreading the gospel._

10. What does Livingstone mean when he says, "We are immortal till our work is done"? _He knew that God held his life in His hands. Nothing could happen to him unless God allowed it._

World Studies

Geography Skills

Case # 3:

The villainous Dr. Distance has been terrorizing the people of Authoria with his long-range water balloon attacks. Several cities have been completely soaked within the last few weeks. Since being assigned to the case, Sir Vey had found few clues—until Al T. Tude showed up. Mr. Tude, a former partner of Dr. Distance, had an argument with him and went to the police. Although Mr. Tude doesn't know where Dr. Distance is, he has a map that gives clues to the next target city. Sir Vey knows that if he can find the city he can figure out where the bombs are coming from and make the arrest.

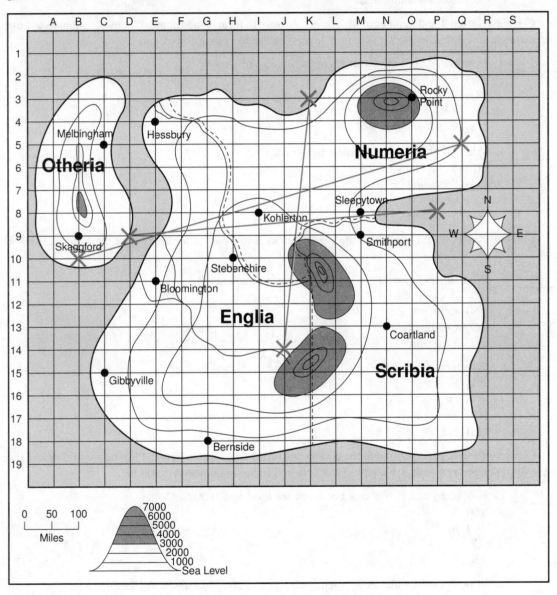

Combine the letter and number of the correct responses to form a coordinate on the map. Plot the coordinate.

<u>K</u>   1. Which country has the highest peak?
      (B) Otheria
      (O) Numeria
      (H) Englia
      (K) Scribia

<u>3</u>   2. Which two countries share a peak?
      (16) Otheria and Numeria
      (3) Englia and Scribia
      (8) Scribia and Otheria
      (5) Numeria and Englia

Combine the letter and number of the correct answers to form a coordinate. Plot the coordinate and then use a straight line to connect it with the coordinate you found in questions 1 and 2.

<u>J</u>   3. How many cities are located within 50 miles of a river?
      (J) 6
      (G) 7
      (Q) 8
      (S) 9

<u>14</u>   4. Which of these cities is closest to Bernside?
      (16) Stebenshire
      (14) Bloomington
      (2) Coartland
      (6) Smithport

Combine the letter and number of the correct answers to form a coordinate. Plot the coordinate on the map.

<u>D</u>   5. What city is found in the Highland climate on the map?
      (D) Rocky Point
      (N) Kohlerton
      (O) Coartland
      (H) Skaggford

<u>9</u>   6. Which country has the smallest amount of Highland climate?
      (1) Englia
      (9) Otheria
      (19) Numeria
      (13) Scribia

Combine the letter and number of the correct answers to form a coordinate. Plot the coordinate and then use a straight line to connect it with the coordinate you found in questions 5 and 6.

<u>P</u>   7. How many cities are located between sea level and 1000 feet?
      (D) 5
      (G) 6
      (P) 7
      (N) 8

<u>8</u>   8. Which of these cities is between 1000 feet and 2000 feet above sea level?
      (13) Kohlerton
      (8) Coartland
      (15) Stebenshire
      (5) Sleepytown

Combine the letter and number of the correct answers to form a coordinate. Plot the coordinate on the map.

_Q_ 9. Approximately how many miles is it from Hessbury to Coartland?
   (I) 50 miles
   (J) 250 miles
   (Q) 500 miles
   (S) 1000 miles

_5_ 10. Which city is 400 miles from Gibbyville?
   (3)   Melbingham
   (13) Smithport
   (16) Bloomington
   (5)   Hessbury

Combine the letter and number of the correct answers to form a coordinate. Plot the coordinate and then use a straight line to connect it with the coordinate you found in questions 9 and 10.

_B_ 11. Which country has the most cities within 50 miles of the coast?
   (F) Otheria
   (E) Numeria
   (B) Englia
   (C) Scribia

_10_ 12. Which city is closest to the Numeria-Englia border?
   (10) Stebenshire
   (14) Smithport
   (15) Hessbury
   (19) Coartland

Look for the triangle inside the three lines you have drawn. What city is located within the triangle?

Kohlerton

The city located there is the site of Dr. Distance's next attack.

World Studies

Causes of Wars

Rarely are wars caused by just one factor. World Wars I and II are no exception. One event may have "sparked" the wars, but there were more issues involved. Examine both wars and how the following categories affected them. Some categories may apply to only one of the wars.

Causes of War	World Wars I & II
Sparks that lit the fuse	WWI—*The assassination of Archduke Francis Ferdinand sparked the war.* WWII—The war began when Hitler invaded Poland in 1939.
Ethnic groups	WWI—*The Slavic people of the Balkans wanted Slavs in Austria-Hungary to be free. Russia declared war on Austria-Hungary because they were Slavs as well.*
Alliances	WWI—*Germany declared war on Russia because of its alliance with Austria-Hungary. France declared war because of its alliance with Russia. Great Britain declared war because of its agreement to protect Belgium.* WWII—*The major alliance of the second world war was between Germany, Italy, and Japan.*
Leaders	WWI—*Wilhelm II of Germany was ready to show that Germans were the most powerful people in Europe.* WWII—*Both Benito Mussolini and Adolf Hitler built up the armies of their nations and prepared them for war.*
Economy	WWII—*The Great Depression created suffering and political instability. In Germany the people were especially willing to listen to Hitler because of the poor economic conditions the Depression had brought.*
Systems of government	WWI—*On one side were military powers that ruled by authority. On the other side were democratic nations.* WWII—*Most of the Axis powers were led by Fascist leaders who believed in glorifying the state.*

World Studies

Chronology

Number each group of events in the order they occurred and place the dates in parentheses. Some events may not have specific dates.

1. __3__ D-day invasion (___1944___)
   __1__ World War I ends (___1918___)
   __2__ Spanish Civil War ends (___1939___)

2. __3__ Ulster revival (___1920s___)
   __2__ Archduke Francis Ferdinand is assassinated (___1914___)
   __1__ Hitler is born (___1889___)

3. __3__ Hitler sends German forces into the Rhineland (___1936___)
   __1__ Poland becomes an independent nation (___1918___)
   __2__ Nazis become largest party in Germany (___1932___)

4. __1__ Germany invades Russia (___June '41___)
   __3__ Allies land in Sicily (___1943___)
   __2__ Japan attacks Pearl Harbor (___Dec. '41___)

5. __1__ World War II begins (___1939___)
   __3__ Common Market is established (___1957___)
   __2__ United Nations is founded (___1945___)

6. __2__ Southern Ireland becomes free (___1921___)
   __1__ World War I begins (___1914___)
   __3__ Beginning of the Great Depression (___late '20s___)

7. __3__ Churchill becomes prime minister (___1939___)
   __1__ Benito Mussolini comes to power (___1923___)
   __2__ Adolf Hitler becomes dictator of Germany (___1933___)

8. __1__ Spanish Civil War begins (___1936___)
   __2__ Hitler annexes Austria (___1938___)
   __3__ France surrenders to Hitler's forces (___1940___)

9. __2__ Vatican II is held (___1960s___)
   __3__ European Union is founded (___1994___)
   __1__ World Council of Churches is established (___1948___)

10. __3__ Francisco Franco dies (___1975___)
    __1__ Adolf Hitler dies (___1945___)
    __2__ Winston Churchill dies (___1965___)

World Studies

Chapter 15   Activity C

Map Study—The Balkans

Refer to text page 422.

1. Use a blue colored pencil to **trace** the national borders dividing the Balkans from the rest of Europe.

2. **Label** these features of physical geography:
   Bodies of Water—Adriatic Sea, Aegean Sea, Ionian Sea, Black Sea, Mediterranean Sea, Sea of Azov, Tyrrhenian Sea
   Rivers—Danube River, Sava River
   Islands—Balearic Islands, Corsica, Crete, Cyprus, Sicily, Sardinia

3. **Label** the following countries:
   Albania, Bosnia and Herzegovina, Bulgaria, Croatia, Greece, Macedonia, Moldova, Romania, Slovenia, Yugoslavia

4. After the assassination of Archduke Francis Ferdinand, Austro-Hungary declared war on Serbia. This country is now part of Yugoslavia. **Place** the powder keg icon in Yugoslavia to represent the event that sparked World War I.

   🛢 powder keg

5. Use a colored pencil to **shade** red the Balkan country that joined the Central Powers in World War I.

Using Additional Resources—

Use an atlas, encyclopedia, or other resources to complete the following.

6. During World War II, Italian forces invaded and conquered Albania. **Place** the Italian and battle icons within Albania to represent this action.

   (IT) Italy

   ✗ battle

7. **Find** out what island the British forces retreated to after Germany defeated the Greeks. **Place** the British icon on this island.

   (GB) Great Britain

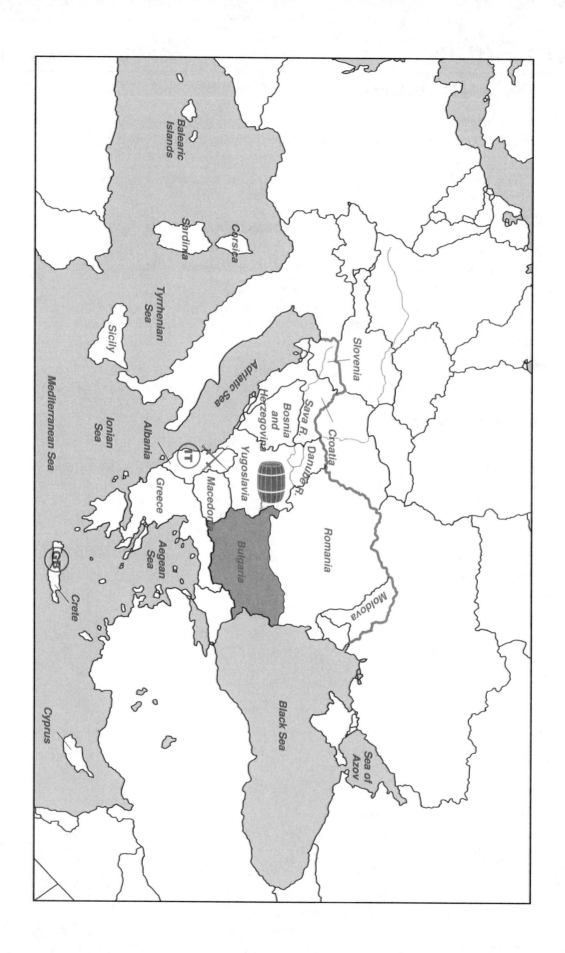

World Studies

Map Study—World Wars I and II

Refer to text pages 421 and 431.

1. Use a red colored pencil to **outline** the maximum area of Axis control in Europe during World War II.

2. Use a red colored pencil to **shade** those countries that were Axis Powers during World War II.

3. **Place** the neutral icon in the three European countries that remained neutral in both World War I and World War II.

    ◻ neutral

4. **Label** these bodies of water:
   Atlantic Ocean, Baltic Sea, Black Sea, Mediterranean Sea, North Sea

5. **Place** the dictator icon in the countries these men were from:
   Francisco Franco, Adolf Hitler, Benito Mussolini

    ▲ dictator

6. **Place** the appropriate icon in the countries these people are best associated with:
   Winston Churchill, T. S. Eliot, Pablo Picasso, Erich Maria Remarque

    / painter

    ✒ writer

    ♛ ruler

Using Additional Resources—

Use an atlas, encyclopedia, or other resources to complete the following.

7. Both Igor Stravinsky and Arnold Schönberg became American citizens during their lifetimes. Find out what countries they were born in and **place** the composer icons in them.

    ♪ composer

8. Use a blue colored pencil to **draw** the path of the Rhine River in Europe.

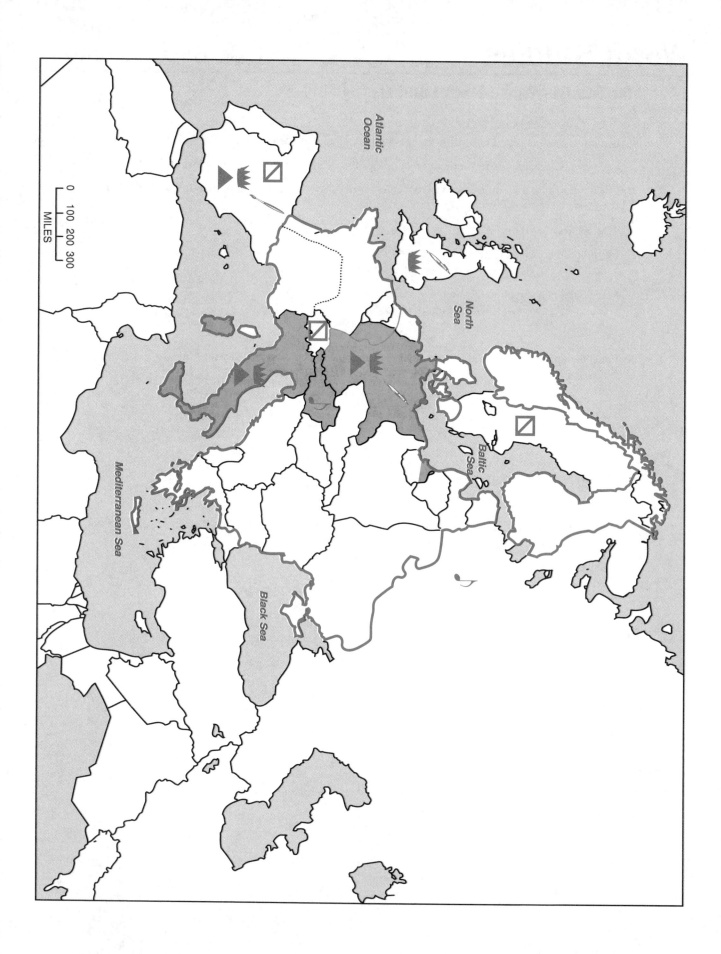

World Studies

Mystery Word

Find the mystery word by answering the questions below and filling in the blanks in the puzzle. The mystery word, spelled vertically in the other answers, is the answer to #11.

1. This composer wrote music having no fixed key.

2. This type of artist tried to capture objects by showing several views at once.

3. This was the nickname of a group of authors who viewed the world pessimistically.

4. This composer wrote pieces using several keys at once.

5. He wrote the novel *All Quiet on the Western Front*.

6. He was the best known Cubist painter.

7. One of his paintings shows watches melting and dripping off tables.

8. This American living in Paris wrote *The Sun Also Rises*.

9. Painters of this style concentrated on representing their feelings about the objects they painted.

10. This writer's works turned from despair to hope after he became a Christian.

11. This type of artist painted objects in bizarre, unrealistic settings or distorted them.

1. A R N O L D S C H O N B E R G

2. C U B I S T

3. L O S T G E N E R A T I O N

4. I G O R S T R A V I N S K Y

5. E R I C H M A R I A R E M A R Q U E

6. P A B L O P I C A S S O

7. S A L V A D O R D A L I

8. E R N E S T H E M I N G W A Y

9. E X P R E S S I O N I S M

10. T S E L I O T

World Studies

News Articles

Imagine you are a reporter writing about these events just after they occurred. Remember to cover the basic journalistic questions of *who, what, where, when,* and *why.* For the Battle of Stalingrad, write an article first from the perspective of a German reporter and then as a Russian reporter. For the Cuban Missile Crisis, write first from the perspective of an American reporter and then as a Soviet reporter. Think about the ways different sides might interpret the same event.

Battle of Stalingrad

German View	Russian View
Headline:	**Headline:**
Article: _____	Article: _____
_____	_____
_____	_____
_____	_____
_____	_____
_____	_____
_____	_____
_____	_____
_____	_____
_____	_____

Cuban Missile Crisis

U.S. View	Soviet View
Headline:	**Headline:**
Article: _____	Article: _____
_____	_____
_____	_____
_____	_____
_____	_____
_____	_____
_____	_____
_____	_____
_____	_____
_____	_____

World Studies

Chapter 16   **Activity B**

People, Plans, and Policies

Complete the following chart using the information in your text.

Policy/Plan	Leader	Description
"War Communism"	Vladimir Ilich Lenin	This was pure Communism; the government took control of all businesses, private property, and food.
"peaceful coexistence"	Nikita Khrushchev	This policy was to change the nature of the competition between the two sides in the Cold War. Instead of a military contest, the two sides would compete economically.
Five-Year Plans	Joseph Stalin	This program for industrialization directed factories to produce goods for industry, agriculture, and the military.
glasnost	Mikhail Gorbachev	This reform meant to allow more openness or freedom in the Soviet Union. People were allowed more say in the government, and restrictions on the church were relaxed.
"de-Stalinization"	Nikita Khrushchev	This policy was a reaction against the harsh policies of Stalin. It allowed more openness in Soviet society.
"New Economic Policy"	Vladimir Ilich Lenin	This was old capitalism in disguise. Farmers could sell some produce, and merchants could make profits. The government also made foreign investments.
détente	Leonid Brezhnev	This policy was supposed to be a relaxing of tensions between the two sides in the Cold War. However, many saw it as a smokescreen to hide Soviet expansion.
perestroika	Mikhail Gorbachev	This reform was meant to restructure the Soviet economy through improved technology and increased productivity. Government interference was also reduced.
collectivization	Joseph Stalin	This system took land from farm owners and joined it into large farms run by the government. Farmers were assigned to work these farms for low wages.

Read each statement and decide who would have said it. Write the correct answer in the blank.

Leonid Brezhnev	1. I sent the army into Czechoslovakia to stop a reform movement.
Mikhail Gorbachev	2. A few days after I resigned on December 25, 1991, the Soviet Union ceased to exist.
Joseph Stalin	3. I encouraged Protestant groups to form the Union of Evangelical Christians—Baptists.
Aleksandr Kerensky	4. After the Russian people overthrew the czar, I became the head of the new Provisional Government.
Nikita Khrushchev	5. I was sent to live in exile after the Cuban Missile Crisis.
Vladimir Ilich Lenin	6. I believed violence might be used to help a revolution to arise.
Cyril Lucar	7. As Patriarch of Constantinople, I tried to introduce Protestant reform into the Orthodox Church.
Aleksandr Solzhenitsyn	8. Once a prisoner myself, I wrote a novel that criticized the Soviet labor camps.

World Studies

Chapter 16   **Activity C**

Map Study—Russia

Refer to text pages 452 and 607.

1. **Label** Russia and use a colored pencil to shade it blue.

2. **Label** these features of physical geography:
   Bodies of Water—Aral Sea, Baltic Sea, Bering Sea, Black Sea, Caspian Sea, Norwegian Sea, Sea of Japan, Sea of Okhotsk
   Mountains—Caucasus Mountains, Ural Mountains
   Regions—Kaliningrad, Siberia

3. **Label** the following countries which were once part of the Soviet Union. Use a colored pencil to **shade** them green:
   Armenia, Azerbaijan, Belarus, Estonia, Georgia, Kazakhstan, Kyrgyzstan, Latvia, Lithuania, Moldova, Turkmenistan, Ukraine, Uzbekistan

4. **Label** the following countries:
   China, Finland, Japan, Mongolia, North Korea, Norway, Poland, South Korea, Sweden

5. **Place** the prison camp icon in the part of the Soviet Union to which Stalin sent soldiers returning from World War II.

   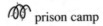 prison camp

Using Additional Resources—

Use an atlas, encyclopedia, or other resources to complete the following.

6. **Find** out where Stalingrad (now Volgograd) is within Russia and then **locate** and **label** it on the map. **Place** the battle icon next to it along with the icon of the nation that attacked it in World War II.

    battle

   (G) Germany

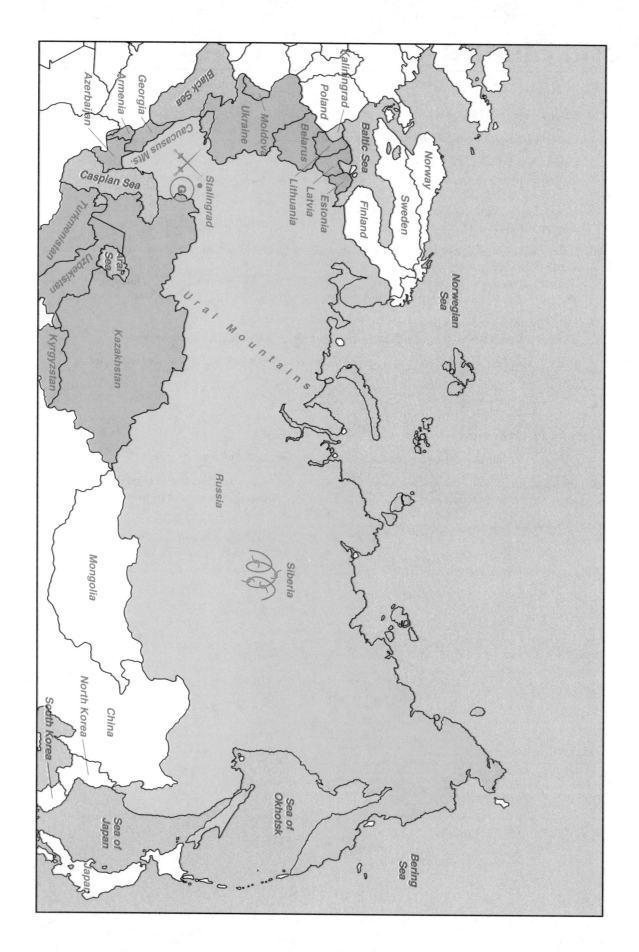

World Studies

Chapter 16   **Activity D**

Map Study—The Cold War

Refer to text page 458.

1. **Label** these bodies of water:
   Atlantic Ocean, Baltic Sea, Black Sea, Mediterranean Sea

2. **Label** the following countries included in NATO:
   Denmark, France, Great Britain, Greece, Iceland, Italy, Norway, Portugal, Spain, Turkey, West Germany

3. **Label** the following countries that were included in the Warsaw Pact:
   Bulgaria, Czechoslovakia, East Germany, Hungary, Poland, Romania, U.S.S.R.

4. Use colored pencils to **shade** the NATO countries blue and the Warsaw Pact countries red.

5. **Label** those Communist countries outside the Warsaw Pact and use a colored pencil to **shade** them yellow.

6. **Create** a key to go along with the numbers 4 and 5.

Using Additional Resources—

Use an atlas, encyclopedia, or other resources to complete the following.

7. **Place** battle icons inside Hungary and Czechoslovakia to represent the movements that were crushed by the Soviet Union. **Find** the names of the leaders who led these movements.

   ⚔ battle *Irme Nagy (Hungary)*
   Alexander Dubcek (Czechoslovakia)

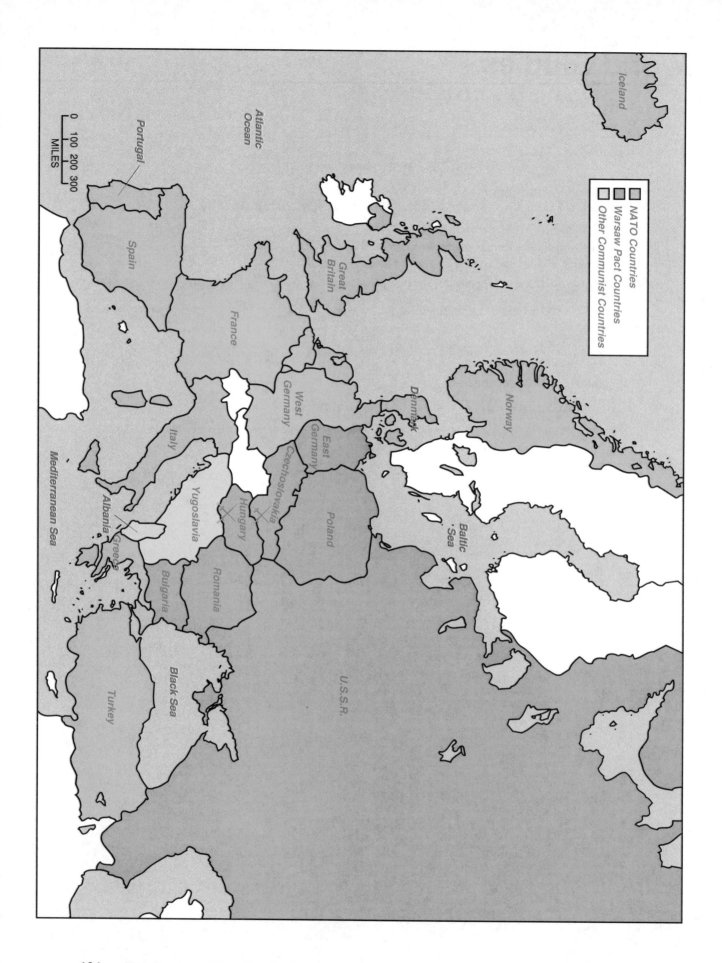

World Studies

Cause and Effect

For each of the following events fill in the cause, year, and effect.

Cause	Event	Year	Effect
The British had established salt laws which said the Indians could buy only government-approved salt on which taxes had been paid.	Gandhi's march to the sea	1930	The march succeeded in drawing worldwide attention to Gandhi and his cause of independence for India.
Japan was greedy for land and needed food. Not enough food was being produced, and the growing population was expanding beyond the country's means.	Japanese invasion of Manchuria	1931	The attack was successful. Japan soon became a military dictatorship allied with Germany and Italy in World War II.
With aid from German army advisors, Chiang Kai-shek's forces surrounded and nearly destroyed the Communist forces of Mao Zedong.	Long March	1934	Eighty thousand Communist soldiers died, but the nucleus of the army survived and was able to fight on.
Japan sought to prevent American intervention in their conquests.	Attack on Pearl Harbor	1941	A large portion of the U.S. Navy in the Pacific was damaged or destroyed. The United States entered World War II on the side of the Allies.
Mao Zedong wanted to reorganize Chinese agriculture and industry	Great Leap Forward	1950	A famine killed more than nineteen million Chinese.
Students desired more reform of corruption and greater political freedom	Tiananmen Square demonstration	1989	Two thousand people were killed in the putting down of the protest.

World Studies

China's Wars

Use encyclopedias, the Internet, or any other resources to find the following information on the Korean War and Vietnam War.

Korean War

Years of war: _1950-53_   Number of casualties:
South Korea/United States/Other U.N. Nations   _580,135_
China/North Korea   _1,591,000_

Write a sentence or two on the significance of the following to the war.

Pusan Perimeter: _This was a battle perimeter in the southeastern corner of South Korea. The farthest Communist advance was stopped here by U.N. forces._

General Douglas MacArthur: _He served as commander of the United Nations forces in the Korean War._

Inchon landing: _This was a surprise landing by U.S. amphibious forces. The troops that landed were able to cut off North Korean forces threatening the Pusan Perimeter._

Harry S. Truman: _He was the president who ordered U.S. forces into Korea. In a controversial move later in the war, he removed General MacArthur from command._

"MIG Alley": _In this area between the Yalu River and Pyongyang, the majority of air battles took place._

"Frozen Chosin": _Chinese forces surrounded MacArthur's army around the Chosin reservoir. In bitterly cold weather, the U.S. forces moved back to Hungnam and were eventually evacuated._

Vietnam War

Years of war: _1946-73_   Number of casualties:
United States/South Vietnam   _1,358,000_
North Vietnam   _500,000-1 million_

Write a sentence or two on the significance of the following to the war.

Gulf of Tonkin: _President Johnson warned the North Vietnamese after a U.S. destroyer was attacked here. Following a reported second attack, Johnson ordered air strikes and increased U.S. involvement in Vietnam._

Ho Chi Minh Trail: _This was the route North Vietnamese troops followed in Cambodia to join and fight with the rebel Viet Cong forces in South Vietnam._

Tet Offensive: _This was a major offensive launched by the Viet Cong and Communist forces on major South Vietnamese cities. Although the offensive failed, the great cost in human lives led to peace talks soon after._

Richard M. Nixon: _After he won election in 1968, Nixon gradually began to remove U.S. forces from Vietnam. However, some felt his decision to clear out supply centers in Cambodia actually expanded the war._

Agent Orange: _This was a weedkiller used by U.S. forces to kill jungle vegetation and reveal Communist hiding places. It was also used to destroy enemy crops. Exposure to it resulted in health problems later._

Henry A. Kissinger: _He was Nixon's chief foreign policy advisor. In 1973 a cease-fire agreement was worked out by him and Le Duc Tho of North Vietnam._

Viet Cong: _These were forces within South Vietnam that opposed the government of President Ngo Dinh Diem. They were under Communist control._

World Studies

Chapter 17   **Activity C**

Map Study—Japan

Refer to text pages 483 and 486.

1. **Label** Japan and use a colored pencil to shade it green.

2. **Label** the following bodies of water:
   East China Sea, Pacific Ocean, Sea of Japan, Sea of Okhotsh, Yellow Sea

3. **Label** the following countries:
   China, North Korea, Russia, South Korea

4. **Label** the following islands of Japan:
   Hokkaido, Honshu, Kyushu, Shikoku

5. Use a blue colored pencil to **shade** the mainland area taken over by Japan in 1910.

Using Additional Resources—

Use an atlas, encyclopedia, or other resources to complete the following.

6. **Find** the cities of Hiroshima and Nagasaki in Japan and then **locate** and **label** each on your map.
   Place the bomb icon by both sites to represent the atomic bombs dropped there.

    bomb

7. **Find** Mt. Fuji and then **locate** and **label** it on your map.

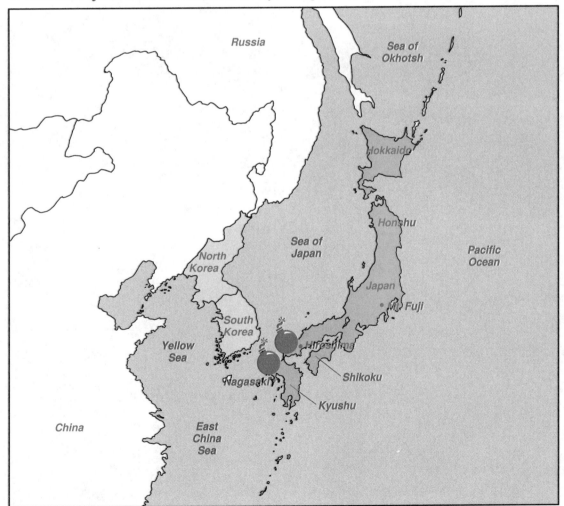

World Studies

Map Study—World War II in the East

Refer to text page 485.

1. **Label** the following countries:
   Australia, China, India, French Indochina, Japan, Mongolia, Burma, Philippines

2. **Label** the following islands in the Pacific:
   Aleutian Islands, Hawaiian Islands, Mariana Islands, Solomon Islands

3. **Label** the following bodies of water:
   Coral Sea, Indian Ocean, Pacific Ocean

4. Use a red colored pencil to **draw** the line showing the farthest Japanese expansion in the Indian and Pacific Oceans. **Place** the Japan icon in the territory inside the line.

   (J) Japan

5. **Write** Gandhi's name in the country he helped bring to independence. **Place** the nation icon of the country he protested against.

   (GB) Great Britain

6. **Locate** and **label** the city of Beijing (Peking). **Place** the battle icon here to represent Tiananmen Square in 1989.

   ✗ battle

Using Additional Resources—

Use an atlas, encyclopedia, or other resources to complete the following.

7. **Place** battle icons in the appropriate countries to represent the Korean War and the Vietnam War.

   ✗ battle

8. **Place** the missionary icon in the country John Sung was from. **Place** smaller missionary icons in the countries and areas where he made preaching tours.

   ✚➔ missionary

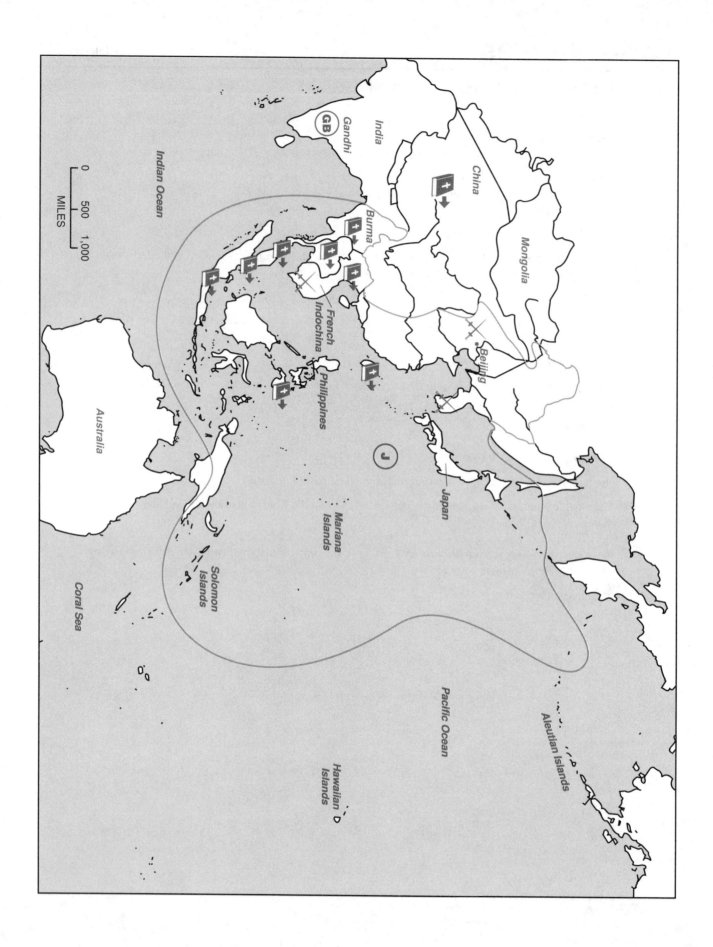

World Studies

Chapter 17   **Activity E**

Japan or China

Decide whether each statement refers to China or Japan. Place your answers in the blanks.

Japan	1.	Their fleet was defeated by the Americans in the Battle of Midway.
Japan	2.	Commodore Matthew Perry opened this country to trade.
China	3.	As this country's leader, Deng Xiaoping promised to reform this country's economy.
China	4.	This country sent Communist forces into Korea to keep the war going.
Japan	5.	After World War II it adopted the capitalism of the West.
Japan	6.	Its emperor announced on the radio that he was not a god.
China	7.	Chiang Kai-shek and his nationalist forces fought to stop the Communists in this country.
Japan	8.	It attacked Manchuria prior to World War II.
China	9.	Sun Yat-sen became leader after the people revolted against the Manchu government.
China	10.	Ni To-sheng and John Sung were both important Christian leaders within this country.
Japan	11.	From the Middle Ages to the 1800s, the real ruling power in this country was the shogun.
Japan	12.	In 1940, it entered World War II on the side of the Axis.
China	13.	After the 1911 revolution, there was a period of great freedom of religion in this country.
China	14.	It regained lost territory after World War II.
Japan	15.	Electronics has been a special strength of its industry.

World Studies

Chapter 18   Activity A

Compare and Contrast

Compare and contrast each pair by listing their characteristics in the columns provided.

Compare and Contrast	
Reform Judaism	**Orthodox Judaism**
• allows Jews to adapt worship to the age they are living in • *temples look similar to Christian churches* • *services are in the native language instead of Hebrew* • *less concern about traditional dietary laws* • *ordains women as rabbis*	• *strictest form of Judaism* • *insists on strict adherence to the law* • *forbids marriage to non-Jews* • *encourages traditional Jewish clothing* • *the Hasidim is a strict form of Orthodox Judaism*
Sunnite Muslims	**Shiite Muslims**
• *make up 90 percent of the world's Muslim population* • *view the caliphs as the legitimate successors to Muhammad* • *developed a system of Islamic law called the shari'a* • *the Wahhabis in Saudi Arabia are a strict form of Sunnite Islam*	• *believe only direct descendants of Muhammad should be leaders of Islam* • *awaiting the return of the twelfth imam* • *majority of the population in Iran, Iraq, and Bahrain* • *the Druze are a splinter group of Shiite Islam in Syria and Lebanon*
Khomeini's "Islamic republic"	**Atatürk's secular state**
• *everyone must live according to the Islamic law* • *Western ideas are considered corrupt and devilish* • *women required to wear heavy veils of Islamic custom* • *Khomeini had officials from the shah's government executed*	• *all religions are supposedly equal* • *modeled after powerful Western nations* • *women given vote, allowed to hold office, and not required to wear a veil* • *Atatürk had enemies tried and executed*
Sephardic Jews	**Ashkenazic Jews**
• *roots are in medieval Spain and Portugal and the Jews who lived in Babylon during the exile*	• *roots in medieval northern and eastern Europe* • *traditions go back to the Jews who lived in Palestine* • *have generally provided the leadership in Israel*

World Studies

Middle East Review

Write the answers to the following statements in the blanks provided.

A. In this war, Egypt, Jordan, Syria, Lebanon, and Iraq all sent troops against Israel. _War of Independence_

B. In this war, several nations fought against Iraq after it invaded Kuwait and threatened oil supplies. _Gulf War_

C. In this war, Israel struck first against Egypt, Syria, and Jordan. _Six-Day War_

D. In this war, Egypt and Syria planned a surprise attack on the Jewish Day of Atonement. _Yom Kippur War_

E. After a popular uprising overthrew the shah, this person began to establish a strict Muslim state in Iran. _Ayatollah Ruholla Khomeini_

F. He established the independent kingdom of Saudi Arabia. _Abdul Aziz ibn-Saud_

G. This substance, discovered in the Persian Gulf, became an enormous source of wealth for Saudi Arabia. _oil_

H. Mustafa Kemal's forces captured Smyrna and drove this group out of Asia Minor. _the Greeks_

I. The oil-producing nations of the Middle East formed this organization to increase their profits and power. _OPEC_

J. Saddam Hussein attacked this country to seize an important waterway and to stop the spread of revolutionary ideas. _Iran_

Match the letters from the questions with the appropriate date below.

1922	1932	1938	1948	1960	1967	1973	1979	1980	1991
H	F	G	A	I	C	D	E	J	B

World Studies

Map Study—Lebanon

Refer to text pages 529 and 540.

1. **Label** Lebanon and use a colored pencil to **shade** it green.

2. **Label** the following countries:
   Cyprus, Egypt, Israel, Iraq, Jordan, Saudi Arabia, Syria, Turkey

3. Use a colored pencil to **shade** red the West Bank and the Gaza Strip.

4. **Place** the Israel and battle icons in those Arab countries involved in the War of Independence. Add a second battle icon in those involved in the Six-Day War and a third for those in the Yom Kippur War.

   ✡ Israel

   ⚔ battle

Using Additional Resources—

Use an atlas, encyclopedia, or other resources to complete the following.

5. **Find** the city the Wailing Wall is located in and then **locate** and **label** it on your map.

6. Use a colored pencil to **shade** blue the part of Egypt that Israel conquered but returned in the Yom Kippur War.

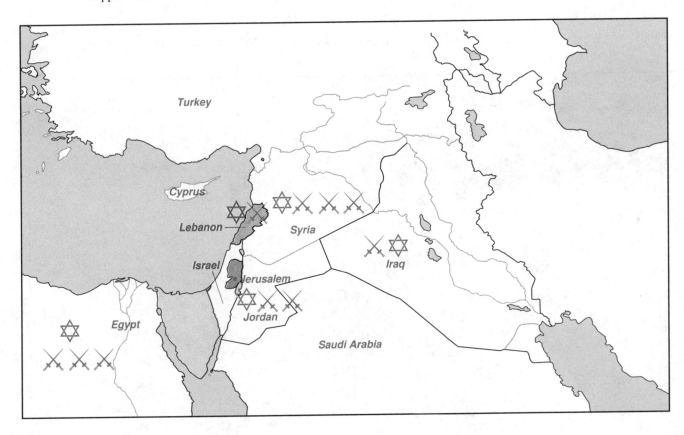

World Studies

Map Study—Middle East

Refer to text pages 514 and 539.

1. **Label** these bodies of water:
   Mediterranean Sea, Red Sea

2. **Label** the following countries:
   Egypt, Iran, Iraq, Saudi Arabia, Syria, Turkey

3. Use a red colored pencil to **shade** the area on the map that was included in the Ottoman Empire.

4. **Place** the oil icon in those areas that are major oil-producing fields in the Middle East.

   ⍦ oil

5. Use a blue colored pencil to **shade** the country where the "White Revolution" took place.

6. Use a green colored pencil to **shade** the country where the Wahhabi movement took place.

7. **Place** the Iraq and battle icons within or next to the two countries invaded by Saddam Hussein.

   Ⓘ Iraq

   ✕ battle

Using Additional Resources—

Use an atlas, encyclopedia, or other resources to complete the following.

8. What body of water is near most of the major oil-producing fields? **Find** its name and then **label** it on your map.

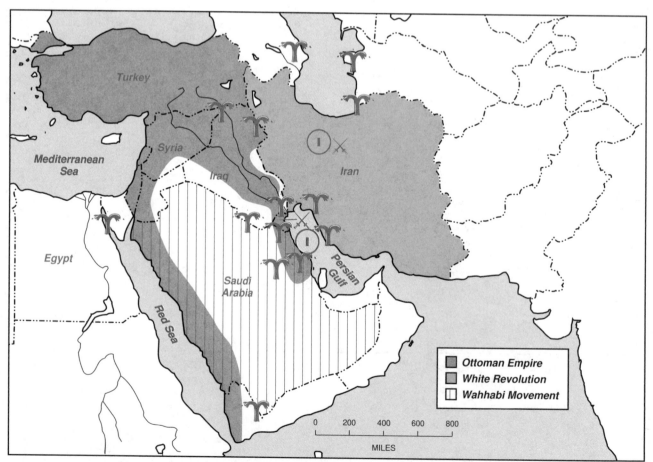

World Studies

Chapter 19   Activity A

Connections

For each pair of terms write a few sentences explaining their relationship to each other.

1. Ethiopian Orthodox Church—*abuna*:   *The abuna is the head of the Ethiopian Orthodox Church. Until 1959 the Coptic Church appointed someone to the position.*

2. Zionist churches—Simon Kimbangu: *Often Zionist churches look to one outstanding individual for leadership. One Zionist church, the Kimbanguist Church, is centered on one such leader—Simon Kimbangu.*

3. Kwame Nkrumah—Communism: *While Nkrumah was studying in the United States and Great Britain, he joined the Communist Party. Later, while he was visiting Communist China, the army overthrew him and his government in Ghana.*

4. Nelson Mandela—*Umkonto we Sizwe*:   *Nelson Mandela formed the Umkonto we Sizwe as a radical branch of the African National Congress. Through it he advocated violence and the overthrow of South Africa's white government.*

5. F. W. de Klerk—Nobel Peace Prize: *As prime minister of South Africa, de Klerk began to reform the country by repealing the apartheid laws and releasing Nelson Mandela from prison. Both he and Mandela received the Nobel Peace Prize in 1994 for their efforts to heal the divisions within South Africa.*

6. Mussolini—Ethiopia: *Italian leader Benito Mussolini went to war with Ethiopia in 1935. The war was successful, but when World War II began, Italian supply lines were disrupted. Ethiopia was liberated in 1941 by British and African troops.*

7. Front for National Liberation—terrorism: *The Front for National Liberation used terrorist activities to further their cause—Algerian independence. Both Muslims and Europeans were killed through their acts. When the FNL came to power, they found themselves victims of terrorist attacks in Algeria.*

8. Charles de Gaulle—decolonization: *When Charles de Gaulle became president of France, he attempted to decolonize Algeria. Despite the opposition of his army, Algeria became an independent nation in 1962.*

9. Hutus—genocide: *During the civil war in Rwanda, the Hutus made an attempt at genocide. Their goal was to wipe out the Tutsis, who were fighting them for control of the country.*

10. Janani Luwum—East Africa Revival: *The East Africa Revival began in the 1920s among Anglican evangelicals. Through it many African religious leaders came to Christ, including Archbishop Jawani Luwum of Uganda.*

World Studies

Multiple Matching

For each group, match the terms with the statements. Place the letters in the spaces provided.

Matching 1: People

A. Charles de Gaulle
B. F. W. de Klerk
C. Haile Selassie
D. Kwame Nkrumah
E. Nelson Mandela
F. W. E. B. Du Bois

___C___ 1. He appealed to the League of Nations when Italy invaded his country of Ethiopia.

___D___ 2. The longer he ruled Ghana, the more he became a dictator.

___B___ 3. He was an Afrikaner prime minister of South Africa.

___F___ 4. He was a major leader in the "Pan-Africanism" movement.

___E___ 5. He advocated violence and the overthrow of the white government in South Africa.

___A___ 6. He pushed for Algerian independence from France.

Matching 2: Organizations and Groups

A. African National Congress
B. Afrikaners
C. "coloureds"
D. Front for National Liberation
E. Hutu
F. Rwandan Patriotic Front
G. Tutsi

___D___ 7. They were dedicated to winning Algerian independence.

___F___ 8. Formed to overthrow the government, this group took over Rwanda in 1994.

___G___ 9. These tall people once ruled Rwanda as an aristocracy.

___B___ 10. The Dutch settlers of Southern Africa were known by this name.

___C___ 11. People of mixed racial heritage in South Africa are known by this name.

___A___ 12. This group was formed to protest the apartheid laws in South Africa.

___E___ 13. Extremists from this group shot down the plane carrying the president of Rwanda.

Matching 3: Processes, Policies, and Movements

A. apartheid
B. assimilation
C. decolonization
D. genocide
E. "Pan-Africanism"
F. "second independence"
G. tribalism

___G___ 14. This conflict among African people is sometimes called regionalism.

___B___ 15. France followed this policy in trying to make Algeria part of the nation.

___D___ 16. This is the destruction of a whole ethnic or racial group.

___E___ 17. This movement presented Africa as a fatherland to all blacks.

___A___ 18. This policy was supposed to provide for separate ethnic development in South Africa.

___C___ 19. The breakup of European empires in Africa was known as this process.

___F___ 20. The African movement away from one-party dictatorships in the 1990s has been called by this name.

Skill: Comprehension

World Studies

Map Study—Democratic Republic of Congo

Refer to text page 548.

1. **Label** the Democratic Republic of Congo and use a colored pencil to **shade** it green.

2. **Label** the following bodies of water:
   Atlantic Ocean, Indian Ocean

3. Use a blue colored pencil to **label** the Congo River and **trace** its route.

4. **Label** the following countries:
   Angola, Burundi, Cameroon, Central African Republic, Equatorial Guinea, Ethiopia, Gabon, Ghana, Kenya, Malawi, Republic of Congo, Rwanda, Sudan, Tanzania, Uganda, Zambia

5. Use a red colored pencil to **shade** the country which has been the center of the conflict between the Tutsis and Hutus.

6. **Place** the revival icon in the three countries where the East Africa Revival was centered.
   ʻ✝ʻ revival

7. Use a yellow colored pencil to **shade** the country that was once known as the Gold Coast.

Using Additional Resources—

Use an atlas, encyclopedia, or other resources to complete the following.

8. **Label** the following lakes within Africa:
   Lake Nyasa, Lake Tanganyika, Lake Victoria

9. Most of the copper and cobalt found within the Democratic Republic of Congo is found in the Katanga Province. **Place** the icons for these resources in this general area of the country.

   Cu copper

   Co cobalt

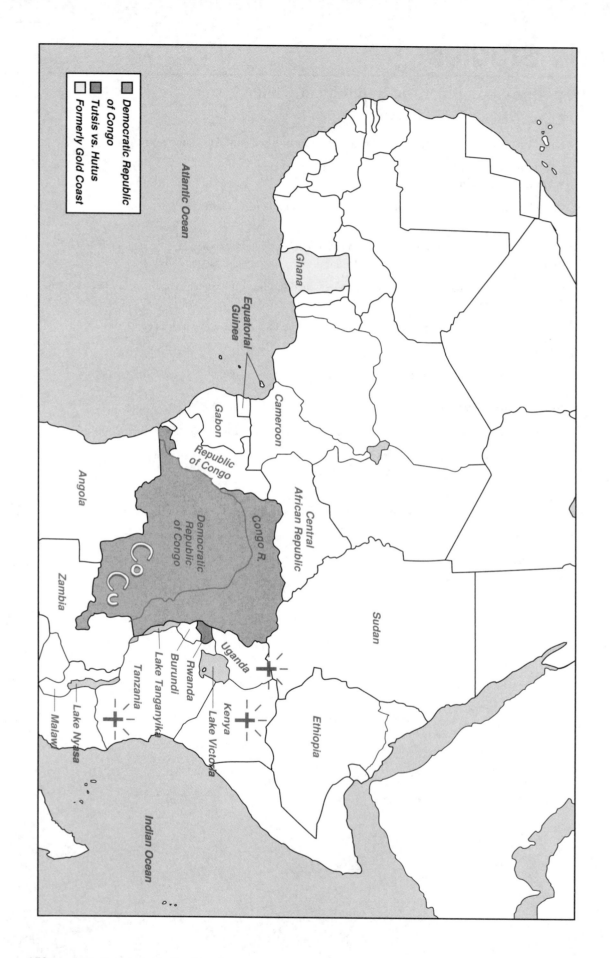

Legend:
- Democratic Republic of Congo
- Tutsis vs. Hutus
- Formerly Gold Coast

Atlantic Ocean

Ghana

Equatorial Guinea

Cameroon

Gabon

Republic of Congo

Angola

Democratic Republic of Congo

Congo R.

Central African Republic

Sudan

Zambia

Congo
Congo

Uganda

Rwanda

Burundi

Lake Tanganyika

Tanzania

Kenya

Lake Victoria

Ethiopia

Malawi

Lake Nyasa

Indian Ocean

World Studies

Chapter 19   Activity D

Decolonization

The following chart shows when the countries in Africa received their independence and from what nation. Fill in the blanks on the chart using the information in Chapter 19.

Country	Date	Colonial Power
Algeria	*1962*	*France*
Angola	1975	Portugal
Benin	1960	France
Botswana	1966	Britain
Burkina Faso	1960	France
Burundi	1962	Belgium
Cape Verde Islands	1975	Portugal
Cameroon	1960	France
Central African Republic	1960	France
Chad	1960	France
Congo	1960	France
Comoros	1975	France
Cote d'Ivoire	1960	France
Democratic Republic of Congo	*1960*	*Belgium*
Djibouti	1977	Ethiopia & Somalia
Egypt	1922	Britain
Equatorial Guinea	1968	Portugal
Eritrea	1993	Ethiopia
Gambia	1965	Britain
Ghana	*1957*	*Britain*
Guinea-Bissau	1974	Portugal
Kenya	1963	Britain
Lesotho	1966	Britain
Libya	1952	Britain & France
Madagascar	1960	France

Country	Date	Colonial Power
Malawi	1964	Britain
Mali	1960	France
Mauritania	1960	France
Mauritius	1992	Britain
Morocco	1956	France & Spain
Mozambique	1974	Portugal
Namibia	1990	Cuba & Angola
Niger	1960	France
Nigeria	1960	Britain
Rwanda	*1962*	*Belgium*
São Tomé and Princípe	1975	Portugal
Senegal	1960	France
Seychelles	1976	Britain
Sierra Leone	1961	Britain
Somalia	1960	Britain
South Africa	1961	Britain
Sudan	1956	Britain & Egypt
Swaziland	1968	Britain
Tanzania	1964	Britain
Togo	1960	France
Tunisia	1956	France
Uganda	1962	Britain
Zambia	1964	Britain
Zimbabwe	1980	Britain

Use the chart on the previous page to answer the following questions.

1. In which decade did most of the countries receive their independence? _the 1960s_

2. From what two colonial powers did most African countries gain their independence? _Britain and_
    France

3. Which of the countries shown was the first to gain independence? What year? _Egypt; 1922_

4. Look at the first four countries to gain their independence. Where are these countries generally located
    in Africa? (use a map to help you) _northern Africa_

5. To what countries did Belgium grant independence? _Burundi, Democratic Republic of Congo, and_
    Rwanda

6. Look at those countries that gained their independence in the 1970s. From what colonial power did
    the majority of them become independent? _Portugal_

7. Why do you think this nation (from the previous question) retained its colonies so long? _Answers_
    will vary. Portugal, as a smaller country, may have relied more on the resources from its colonies.

8. Why are Ethiopia and Liberia excluded from this list? You may need to look back in previous chapters
    to find this information. _Ethiopia has been independent since the days of the Roman Empire. Although_
    it was invaded by Italy in the 1930s, the country was liberated in 1941. Liberia was established in 1821 as a
    home for former slaves. It has remained independent since then.

9. Why do you think Britain, France, and other colonial powers decided to give independence to these
    countries in Africa? _Answers will vary. The cost of maintaining the colonies may have become greater_
    than the profits from them. Independence movements within some countries may have made them difficult
    to govern.

World Studies

Chapter 20   Activity A

Jim Elliot

Read these portions of Jim Elliot's diary and then answer the questions.

January 1, 1952

No small sign was given me confirming my going to Ecuador via the *Santa Juana* [a Grace Line freighter]. I have been asking God to seal my leaving, not knowing what to expect. Yesterday several checks came in the mail, and I intended to cash them and send a bank check to Kelley for my passage. But the bank was closed when I finally found a parking place and finished other pressing things yesterday afternoon. Today when I picked up some purchases from Tommy Dryden, he gave me a check for $50. I made no special note of it until I got home and put it with those I got in yesterday's mail. Then I discovered that they totaled $315, my exact fare to Guayaquil! All in twenty-four hours, from five separate sources. This is the first of these miracles I am encouraged to expect. Hallelujah! Praise to the King of heavenly coffers. . . . Wise Guide, my God. This to encourage me for 1952.

March 2

Lord's Day morning. Great sense of uselessness because of inner failure and sin. Reading in the Law and in the Psalms, but with no life. My soul refuses comfort and instruction. Revive Thy servant, Lord God; restore his soul. Don't feel that I'm getting anywhere, either in the Word or in Spanish. . . . Doctor Paul Roberts's slides on the work in Ecuador were good—longing, though, for a word from God. All the lesser blessings and comforts fail in my mind. Out of the depths have I called unto Thee, O Lord, hear Thou my cry.

March 6

And today I asked in faith for three things. First, a Latin young fellow to converse with in Spanish and contact for the Lord. He was in T's study before noon, and I spent an hour and a half with him in the plaza this afternoon. Abdón, he is, from San Miguel. Second, that I could get the recorder to work right. I did—before noon. It was unaffected by the transportation handling of the barrel. Third, *El Camino Real*, a textbook for Spanish. This has not come yet, but I expect it. For I believe Him who said, "Porque de cierto os digo que cualquiera que dijere a este monte: Quítate, y échate en la mar, y no dudare en su corazón, mas creyere que será hecho lo que dice, lo que dijire le será hecho" (Mark 11:23).

March 8

Met and chatted with Misses Hatley and Hernandez, Jehovah's Witnesses who are daily in the plaza. "Lo here" and "lo there. . . ." point the heretics, poor earth-centered souls, blind leaders who with those who follow teeter on the brink of "the ditch." There are nine such in Quito now. I don't know how many in Guayaquil, Ambato, and Cuenca. Will the cause of Christ be forever so weak? Not that we are so few here, we evangelicals, but that we are of such mediocre stock, so distant from the people, so puny in our efforts. Still, He works on with us; oh, that He might work in *power*.

June 8

Heard brother Crisman (fifty years in Ecuador) at the Second Church in the morning. Lord, let me learn to speak Spanish in fifty years—seems as if no one really gets past the beginner's stage of pronunciation of all the gringos I've met. And none hit the national's genius of language. Giver of the gift of tongues! Let me speak to them as they ought to be spoken to, so they do not have to hide their reaction with polite praise. Glad to be in a national home—at least to hear it spoken as a living-thought medium—not merely as English translation.

July 2

Buzzed Shell's deserted field at Ayuy; landed at Villano for lunch in the *guarnición*. Made inquiries about Quichua population in the Canelos region. Estimates uncertain. Would guess one thousand to fifteen hundred.

September 14

More than fifty Indians came to the singing and Gospel teaching this morning, and that after the priest had made special efforts yesterday to get them to the mass. He blundered on us as we were listening to an Indian play a violin in a house downriver where we had gone to watch Venancio [an Indian, hired as a handyman] butcher a hog. He refused Pete's hand as he entered, walked to the center of the house, made the brief announcement that all good Christians should go to mass on Sunday, and stalked out the other door.

November 20

The plane turned over on the airstrip and was here a week waiting for repairs. Two Indians died of what we suppose to be the yellow fever—Pedro, a sixteen-year-old who was under the priest's care, and Cesar, a baby not a year old, under ours. Henrique, his father, refused penicillin after an injection abscess developed from a quinine shot. Child died just before we were called; camphor and artificial respiration had no effect in revival. We buried him in a semi-planed box under the school house.

March 2, 1953

Henry Andi died last Friday afternoon—I cannot tell what from. [The Andi family were squatters in Shandia.] Began vomiting great mouthfuls of bright red blood last Monday. We stopped it with Vitamin K and emetine and gave several shots of gluconate. He was getting along fine until Friday about 3:45 when he vomited again and became exceedingly restless—dangerously so for one so weak. He was gone by 4:30. The first man I ever watched die. And so it will come to me one day, I kept thinking. I wonder if that little phrase I used to use in preaching so much was something of a prophecy: "Are you willing to lie in some native hut to die of a disease American doctors never heard of?" I am still willing, Lord God. Whatever You say shall stand at my end time. But, oh, I want to live to teach Thy Word. Lord, let me live "until I have declared Thy works to this generation."

August 15

Tuesday we took off the girders of the foundation, and in the night I got my first touch of malaria. Ed and Pete left Wednesday morning, and I spent the day in chills and fever, utter weakness, and quite a lot of pain. Managed to get the girders laid for the storage house halfway down the strip. That night I saw the luminous dial on my watch flash as I rolled and read every half hour from midnight to five. Dizziness and headache constant with utter loss of appetite for everything except lemonade, which, for the gallons I have drunk to cool and fill and satisfy me these three days, I regard as a rich mercy from God. There is a teapot on the desk about a third full now.

July 19, 1955

Venancio Tapai and I baptized fourteen this morning after the Gospel meeting. . . .

And there was enough of the physically distracting this morning to save one from walking on clouds. A part of the cliff gave way, and three girls sat down on the beach amid shrieks of laughter. The schoolboys threw stones in the water. Antonia's son fell headlong off the airstrip onto the beach and set up a great wail just as she was being baptized. Venancio failed to get Carmel Chimbu's face under. A group of mockers from the priest's came by and taunted the baptized ones about bathing with their clothes on. But God is my witness that I have fulfilled His Word as I knew how. . . . Praise to His Name! He only does wonders.

October 29

First time I ever saw an Auca—fifteen hundred feet is a long ways if you're looking out of an airplane. Nate and Ed have found two sites and have been visiting one and dropping gifts weekly for about a month.

Ed and I flew to Villano with Johnny [Keenan, a MAF pilot] on Thursday and arrived at the Huito Plaza around 4:30 P.M. or later. . . . Had a meeting—perhaps forty persons Friday morning on the church benches in the plaza. As we were visiting in the afternoon, a small boy—perhaps ten years old—named Adam, was pulled under, evidently by a boa, and drowned while swimming. The search for recovery of and wake-making over his body spoiled the afternoon meeting we planned. Indians claimed a *supai* [a demon (Quichua)] got him. . . . Returned to Villano by canoe 6:30-8:15 A.M. Saturday. Nate was waiting for us.

Questions

1. How did Elliot get to Ecuador? How did he know God wanted him to travel this way? _Elliot_ _travelled by sea on a Grace Line freighter; He knew this was God's will because God provided the exact amount of money needed for the ship fare._

2. On March 6, 1952, Elliot quotes Mark 11:23 in Spanish. Look up this verse in a Bible and write it here.
   Mark 11:23 For verily I say unto you, That whosoever shall say unto this mountain, Be thou removed, and be thou cast into the sea; and shall not doubt in his heart, but shall believe that those things which he saith shall come to pass; he shall have whatsoever he saith.

Why did this verse make Elliot believe the textbook would arrive? _Elliot was asking in faith, and he_
knew God could answer his prayer.

3. Look up Matthew 15:14 in a Bible. Whom does Elliot relate this verse to and why? _Elliot refers to_
this verse when talking about the Jehovah's Witnesses in the area. He saw them as blind leaders leading
the people astray.

4. In his June 8 entry, Elliot refers to the Lord as the "Giver of the gift of tongues." How does Elliot's
   statement differ from the Charismatics' view of tongues? _Elliot was recognizing God as the one who_
understands all speech and could help him learn Spanish. He is not referring to the speech and vocal
sounds produced in a state of supposed religious ecstasy.

5. On July 2, 1952, Elliot flew over the deserted airstrip of the Shell company. According to your text,
   what had happened between Shell and the Auca Indians? _Ten years before the missionaries arrived,_
the Aucas had killed eleven employees of the company.

6. How did the Indians explain the death of the boy killed by a boa constrictor? _They believed that a_
demon (supai) had gotten him.
   What does this show about the people? _They had superstitious beliefs._

7. Your text says that the Catholic Church has exercised control over Latin America for a long time. How
   is this evident in the readings? _In one instance the Catholic priest spoke openly against the_
missionaries. He tried to convince the people to go to mass rather than the missionary meetings. During
the baptism, a group of mockers came from the priest.

8. What kinds of physical, mental, and spiritual problems did Elliot personally face in his mission
   efforts? _Answers may vary. Physically, Elliot suffered once from malaria. Mentally, he experienced_
problems trying to learn Spanish to communicate with the Indians. Spiritually, Elliot says he faced "inner
failure and sin" at times.

9. What types of jobs did Elliot do besides holding meetings with the people? _Elliot and the others_
treated Indians who were sick. They also worked on building projects such as the storage house mentioned
on August 15, 1953. Other tasks included scouting out the land from the plane and dropping gifts to make
contact with the Indians.

10. Look at the last sentence of the March 2, 1953 entry. How has the Lord answered this prayer? _Not_
only did Elliot make contact with the Aucas, but his story has reached people all around the world and from
generation to generation.

World Studies

Chapter 20   **Activity B**

Comparing Countries

Find the statistics for each country by looking at an encyclopedia or other outside sources.

Argentina

Area: _____1,072,067 sq mi._____

Population: ___36,265,463_____

Official language: ___Spanish_____

Type of government: ___Republic_____

Costa Rica

Area: _____19,652 sq mi._____

Population: ___3,604,642_____

Official language: ___Spanish_____

Type of government: ___Republic_____

Read each question and answer it in relation to each country. Each answer should be written in complete sentences. Give as much material as possible.

How has military power been used in each country?	
Argentina	**Costa Rica**
Military power has played a very important role in controlling Argentina's politics. In 1930 and in 1943 the army overthrew the government of the country. Juan Perón, a former military officer, held power in the country with the help of the military. Later on, the army attempted to remove him from office. They finally succeeded in 1955. Many of the later presidents were also forced out of office by armed forces. During the "dirty war," Argentina became a military dictatorship.	*In Costa Rica military power has almost always been used only when needed. Figueres used his army to defeat the corrupt government. However, he did not use it to make himself a dictator. Figueres went so far as to abolish the army in Costa Rica. Since then, the only real military power has been a police force of over ten thousand. They are used to maintain order within the country.*

What type of international relations has each of these countries had?	
Argentina	**Costa Rica**
During World War II Argentina remained neutral until it was obvious who would win. Argentina's relations with Great Britain have been most notable. In 1982 Argentinean forces seized the Falkland Islands occupied by the British. In the end, the Argentine forces were forced to surrender and leave the Falklands.	*Costa Rica's relations with the rest of the world have been quite favorable. Since Costa Rica abolished its army, the nation has relied on international organizations such as the Organization of American States for protection. President Oscar Arias Sánchez has attempted to bring peace to all of Central America.*

Juan Perón and Jose Maria Figueres Ferrer have both been presidents in their countries. How did each of them gain the support to be elected?	
Argentina	**Costa Rica**
Perón gained support from both the army and the workers in Argentina. His popularity grew after he helped out in a labor dispute and gave workers minimum wage and paid holidays. The energetic appeal of his wife, Eva, also helped him to become popular.	*Figueres became popular after helping to topple the corrupt government of the country. After reorganizing the government he handed power over to the winner of a recent election. In gratitude the people later elected him twice to the presidency of the country.*

World Studies

Map Study—Brazil

Refer to text page 582.

1. **Label** Brazil and use a colored pencil to **shade** it green.

2. **Label** the following bodies of water:
   Atlantic Ocean, Caribbean Sea, Gulf of Honduras, Pacific Ocean

3. Use a blue colored pencil to **label** and **trace** the route of the Amazon River in South America.

4. **Label** the following countries:
   Argentina, Bolivia, Chile, Colombia, Costa Rica, Ecuador, French Guiana, Guyana, Paraguay, Peru, Suriname, Uruguay, Venezuela

5. Use a blue colored pencil to **shade** the country where Juan Perón was president.

6. Use a red colored pencil to **shade** the Latin American country that was the first to abolish slavery.

7. **Place** the appropriate icon in the South American countries with which these men are associated:
   Jim Elliot, Heitor Villa-Lobos

    missionary

   ♪ composer

Using Additional Resources—

Use an atlas, encyclopedia, or other resources to complete the following.

8. Use a blue colored pencil to **label** and **draw** the path of the Paraná River in South America.

9. **Label** the major mountain range that extends down the western side of South America.

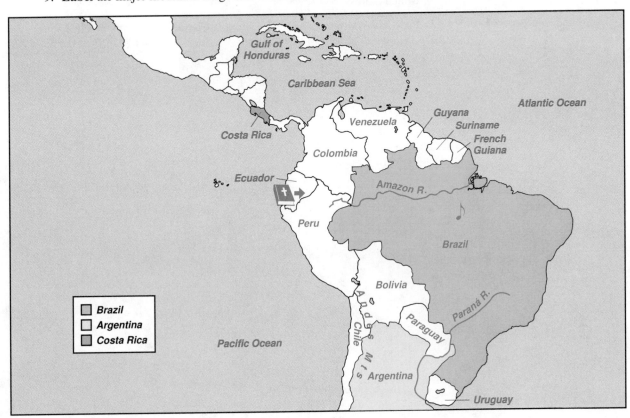

World Studies

Who Am I?—Mexican History

Read each statement and decide whom it refers to. Write the correct answer in the blank. Some names may be used more than once.

Emiliano Zapata	1. I led a peasant uprising in southern Mexico during the Mexican Revolution.
John Pershing	2. I was sent by the U.S. army to track down "Pancho" Villa.
Diego Rivera	3. Along with José Clemente, I painted murals that celebrated Mexico's history and featured the common people.
Venustiano Carranza	4. With the support of the United States, I became president of Mexico after the revolution.
Porfirio Díaz	5. My dictatorship over Mexico collapsed after thirty years of rule.
Emiliano Zapata	6. I was killed in 1919 in an ambush by Carranza's forces.
Victoriano Huerta	7. After having Francisco Madero overthrown and executed, I declared myself dictator of Mexico.
Victoriano Huerta	8. The United States opposed my Mexican government and referred to me as a "desperate brute."
"Pancho" Villa	9. I led revolutionary forces to victory in northern Mexico.
Porfirio Díaz	10. There was an uproar and rebellion after I tried to fix the 1910 election and make myself the winner.
"Pancho" Villa	11. I had sixteen American engineers killed and even led attacks into the United States.
Venustiano Carranza	12. I was killed while trying to flee Mexico City after my army rebelled.

World Studies

Geography Skills

Case #4:

A secret investigation has revealed that Stinky and his gang of clowns are planning another attack. In the past they've released a secret weapon among unsuspecting citizens—laughing gas! Police disguised as circus monkeys managed to make copies of suspected plans for the attack. However, the papers seemed to contain nothing more than unimportant statistics. The GIA called in Sir Vey to work on the case. After studying the statistics, Vey turned to the police and said, "I know the city, the building, the day, and the time they plan to strike." Follow the directions below and see how he cracked the case.

Answer the questions using the corresponding graphs. Then complete the equations using the numbers in parentheses that correspond to the answers.

Bar Graph

1. Which city shown on the bar graph has the lowest population?   *Sydney*

2. What city has a population closest to 14 million?   **Los Angeles**

3. Which city has the second highest population?   *São Paolo*

4. Which city has a population closest to that of Lagos?   *Paris*

5. Which city has the highest population?   *Tokyo*

(answer #1) + (answer #2) + (answer #3) × (answer #4) ÷ (answer #5) =

In which city is the crime going to take place?   *Tokyo*

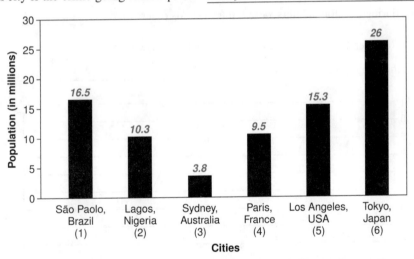

Picture Graph

1. On what day were the most visitors at the zoo?   *Saturday*

2. On what day were 1200 visitors at the zoo?   *Friday*

3. On what day were the fewest visitors there?   *Wednesday*

4. On what day were between 600 and 800 visitors there?   *Tuesday*

5. Did Monday or Thursday have more visitors?   *Thursday*

(answer #1) + (answer #2) − (answer #3) × (answer #4) ÷ (answer #5) =

What day of the week is the crime going to take place?   *Thursday*

Number of Visitors at the Zoo

Monday (1)   🧍🧍🧍🧍🧍🧍🧍🧍🧍   ⑨

Tuesday (2)   🧍🧍🧍🧍🧍🧍🧍   ⑦

Wednesday (3)   🧍🧍🧍🧍🧍   ⑤

Thursday (4)   🧍🧍🧍🧍🧍🧍🧍🧍🧍🧍   ⑩

Friday (5)   🧍🧍🧍🧍🧍🧍🧍🧍🧍🧍🧍🧍   ⑫

Saturday (6)   🧍🧍🧍🧍🧍🧍🧍🧍🧍🧍🧍🧍🧍🧍🧍   ⑮

🧍 = 100 people

Line Graph

1. At what hour were the most customers there?   *12:00 P.M.*

2. At what time after lunch were only eight customers in the store?   *5:00 P.M.*

3. Between 9:00 A.M. and 1:00 P.M., when were the fewest customers in the store?   *10:00 A.M.*

4. At what hour were only four customers in the store?   *7:00 A.M.*

5. At what time during the store's hours were the fewest customers there?   *3:00 P.M.*

(answer #1) × (answer #2) − (answer #3) + (answer #4) ÷ (answer #5) =

What time is the crime going to take place?   *1:00 P.M.*

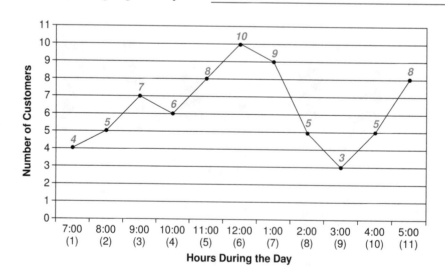

Pie Graph

1. Where were the fewest hot dogs sold? _bank_

2. Where were the most hot dogs sold? _stadium_

3. Which place had more hot dog sales than the courthouse but fewer than the airport? _library_

4. Which place had the third highest amount of hot dog sales? _airport_

5. Which place had half as many hot dog sales as city hall? _embassy_

(answer #1) ÷ (answer #2) + (answer #3) − (answer #4) ÷ (answer #5) = _____

In what building is the crime going to take place? _(city hall)_

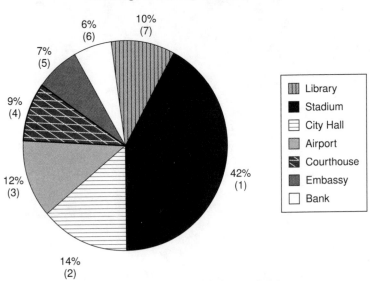

Percentage of Hot Dog Sales in One Day